RAILWAYS GALORE

RAILWAYS GALORE

A GUIDE TO PRESERVED RAILWAYS, MINIATURE RAILWAYS
AND RAILWAY MUSEUMS IN BRITAIN AND IRELAND

EDITED BY CHRISTOPHER AWDRY

B🌾XTREE

First published in Great Britain in 1996 by Boxtree Limited,
Broadwall House, 21 Broadwall, London SE1 9PL

ISBN: 0 7522 1687 2

1 3 5 7 9 10 8 6 4 2

Conceived, compiled and designed by Julian Holland
Edited by Christopher Awdry

Printed and bound in Great Britain by
Butler & Tanner Ltd, Frome and London

Colour origination by Global Colour Separation Sdn Bhd

A CIP catalogue entry for this book is available from the
British Library

Note In time of rapid change within the leisure
railway movement it is difficult to ensure that all
the information given is entirely accurate and up
to date. To avoid disappointment it is always
advisable to telephone for the latest information
before setting off to visit a railway or museum.
Although the publishers can accept no
responsibility for inaccuracies and omissions
they are always grateful for corrections and
suggestions for improvement.

Julian Holland would like to thank the the many
organisations and individuals, too numerous to
mention, who have kindly supplied information
for this book.

Contents

Foreword

Most guides to the railway artefacts in this country tend towards the 'preserved' lines, many of which, strictly, aren't preserved anyway, since they consist, perhaps, of brand new equipment running on a miniature gauge line along a disused BR trackbed. The only 'preserved' part is, of course, the trackbed, still fulfilling its original role. In recent years railways have tended to steer clear of this criticism by calling themselves 'steam' or 'pleasure' lines. Fair enough, but 'preserved' they certainly aren't. So what does constitute a 'preserved' railway? There are probably as many opinions about that as there are people reading these words; I harbour no illusions that everyone who reads this book will necessarily hold the same view as me, and I have, therefore, no intention of forcing my opinion on you. This book has in any case a far wider scope than mere semantics, venturing into the hitherto unploughed fields of miniature lines. It has been both interesting and instructive to discover that many of the smaller-scale lines have been around for longer than one imagined.

Railway preservation began in the United Kingdom as soon as the very early locomotives wore out and were set aside without being scrapped – more of these early engines survive than might be expected, and can be seen in museums in Liverpool, Edinburgh, London, York and Darlington to name but a few. On the whole, although there are some notable gaps, the locomotive history of our railways is well represented. While their story is less cohesive, preservation of smaller locomotives was also taking place on private and industrial sites, and in parks and other municipal locations.

Carriages, for fairly obvious reasons, have survived less well, but a number of lines, notably the Kent & East Sussex and the Isle of Wight Steam Railways, have made it their business to restore 'vintage' stock. The Vintage Carriage Trust (see p.141) too, based at Ingrow on the Keighley & Worth Valley Railway, has done invaluable work in this field.

Most lines have a selection of wagons, many of them rotting gently away. Some have been restored however, and, contrary to perceived opinion, have become a paying part of their railway, enabling revenue to flow in

Opposite Manning Wardle 0-6-0ST No. 14 *Charwelton* hauls a train of vintage coaches on the Kent & East Sussex Railway, July 11 1991 *(Mike Esau)*

from photographers who are prepared to finance special freight days for the benefit of their cameras. Other than this, the only preservation society to make any real use of its wagon collection is the Scottish Railway Preservation Society, which is to be congratulated on setting up its new exhibition, opened in 1995, at Bo'ness – see page 149.

So far as most people are concerned, probably, railway preservation started in 1950, when the Talyllyn Railway began its pioneering effort. The Festiniog followed the TR's lead fairly quickly, and a brand-new narrow gauge line using preserved rolling stock (the Lincolnshire Coast Light Railway) opened in 1960, running southwards from a site near Cleethorpes. By the close of that year there was a total of 48 preservation sites open, of which six were working railways and 16 were museums which had been open prior to 1950. Of the other three lines opened in 1960, two were standard gauge – the Middleton and the Bluebell. The third was the 15in gauge Ravenglass & Eskdale Railway, not so much 'opened' as taken over as a runner by a preservation society.

Even after ten years there was a large body of people who thought the whole idea was mad and that privately-run projects were doomed to failure. In spite of this, growth to 1970 was decidedly quicker. By the end of that year there were no less than 196 sites, 31 of which had opened within the last 12 months. Interestingly, no fewer than 35 had closed in 1970, though it seems curious that none of the pundits, vociferous then as now about 'spreading the jam even thinner' actually seems to have used this statistic as ammunition! During that decade the Festiniog began its fight against the Central Electricity Generating Board for cutting its route by building a reservoir across it above Dduallt, and in 1963 it celebrated the centenary of steam haulage on the line. The Talyllyn also marked a centenary (1965), the Scottish Railway Preservation Society was established, the Severn Valley Railway Association was formed in 1967, and the Welshpool & Llanfair, with army assistance, rebuilt its viaduct across the River Banwy, a major feat of engineering at the time. The Dart Valley Railway, the first preservation project to be run by a commercial company was, with a nice touch of irony

opened by Dr Beeching in 1969. In that year too the Kent & East Sussex people began a long legal wrangle with the Ministry of Transport's refusal of its Light Railway Order, and *Flying Scotsman* was bought from BR by Alan Pegler to begin a far more lively existence than it had ever had before.

Now realisation began to dawn that the railway preservationists really had got something. Proliferation became phenomenal: no fewer than 234 sites opened during the next ten years, the most in any one year (1973) being 35. On the opposite side of the coin, closures totalled 128, with 21 of them in 1973 and 19 in 1977. The number of railways actually operating almost doubled, from 25 in 1969 to 48 ten years later. The Festiniog, having won compensation from the CEGB, set out towards Blaenau, while the Talyllyn extended rather more modestly. The North Norfolk Railway became the first company to offer shares – very successfully. It became the period of the big boys – the West Somerset opened, and also the Severn Valley, an

Above Bassett-Lowke 4-4-2 *Synolda*, built in 1912, on the 15in gauge Ravenglass & Eskdale Railway, August 23 1980 *(R C Riley)*

Opposite LBSCR Class A1X 0-6-0T No. 55 *Stepney* at Sheffield Park on the Bluebell Railway, August 28 1960 *(R C Riley)*   9

Opposite Alan Pegler's LNER Class A3 4-6-2 No. 4472 *Flying Scotsman* passes Upton Scudamore on a main line special, August 16 1964 *(R C Riley)*

enterprise which has expanded steadily ever since. The Main Line Steam Trust took its first steps towards establishing a 'main line' around Loughborough, and the North Yorkshire Moors Railway opened. Arguments began about the route of the bypass round Corfe Castle, and the Midland Railway Centre, supported by Derbyshire County Council, was established at Ripley.

The Seventies became a boom period for locomotives. A total of 104 of all types were taken in hand by preservation groups in 1978 alone, and during the decade a total of 119 main line standard gauge steam engines found a home, with the figures for industrials much higher. It was, of course, the decade in which the idea of railtours began to burgeon, and towards the end of it diesel locomotives began to attract some interest as objects for preservation.

In 1982 the Festiniog completed its magnificent achievement by running a public passenger train into Blaenau Ffestiniog for the first time for 43 years, and the Welshpool & Llanfair reached a new terminus on the outskirts of Welshpool. Three years later the Mid-Hants got to Alton, and in 1986 the Nene Valley Railway extended its service to Peterborough. That was also the same year that the North Norfolk Railway reached Holt, and in 1989 the Bo'ness & Kinneil extended its line to Birkhill. The Bure Valley Railway, opened in 1990, was a bit different, a 15in gauge line laid as a commercial proposition (as opposed to a preserved one) on an old standard gauge trackbed. Subsequent years have not been without their problems.

Projects still come and go, and technology has made enormous strides. From the doubts and fears of those early years the growth in confidence was gradual, increasing in proportion to the number of schemes put forward. Our equipment on the Talyllyn in 1950 was minimal, and while skills were available we lacked both the confidence and facilities to use our expertise. Boston Lodge on the Festiniog Railway, altogether bigger and better fitted out, led the way. Then came the Severn Valley and the North Yorkshire Moors lines, and other, smaller projects – the Bluebell seems to have been the first in this field, back in the mid-Sixties – have meant more 'in-house' overhauls. The Ravenglass & Eskdale people have exported two new steam

locomotives to Japan, both substantially built in its Ravenglass workshop.

Boilers have always been the main problem in the restoration of locomotives, but the expertise in working with them has grown beyond all imagination. The boiler shop at Bridgnorth (Severn Valley Railway) was a major step, and the restoration of *Duke of Gloucester,* mostly at Loughborough, was another. The casting of driving wheels, for long thought impossible, has now been achieved several times, and a new Class A1 Pacific currently under construction, will take the story a stage further. It would indeed be a brave man, who, with hand on heart, nowadays dared say, 'This cannot be done'.

Another development over the years has been a change in the attitude taken to diesel preservation. A few lone voices were raised in the letter pages of the railway press back in the early 1970s, but were not, I think, regarded very seriously. Now diesel locomotives are to be found on most railways, even to the stage that special galas are held to show them off. One or two lines even make a marketing point of the fact that they *don't* use them! Strangely though, some railways have found customer-resistance to diesel locomotives. The West Somerset Railway, among others, found that some potential passengers, on realising that the next available train was scheduled to be a diesel-hauled service, waited for the next, hauled by steam. This is curious, because I have a hunch that if a survey taken among the passengers on a train was to ask what engine was hauling them, a large proportion would neither know nor care.

Diesel locomotives are much more available now, of course, having served their turn on BR and been superseded. And I know of one railway (which had perhaps better remain anonymous) where it is easier to get recruits to work in the diesel section than with steam. I should not be surprised to see this trend grow, and in years to come it is, perhaps, not impossible that the steam men may find themselves in the minority. Not, I hope, to the point where the steam engine becomes secondary, but one never knows. After all, I never dreamt, back in 1960, that I would be writing about preserved diesel engines in 1996!

Opposite Birds-eye view of Kingswear station on the Paignton & Dartmouth Steam Railway *(AA Photo Library)*

Above Preserved GWR 'King' class 4-6-0 No. 6000 *King George V* at Kensington Olympia with the first main line steam-hauled special, October 2 1971 *(R C Riley)*

A topic which has raised a good deal of discussion during the past five years is that of railtours. Back on October 2 1971 *King George V* made its steam-ban-breaking run, at the beginning of a week instigated because, BR said it wanted to '...assess the difficulties involved in running steam-hauled excursions.' Gradually it began to realise that this was a way forward – a limited number of routes was made available for 1972, but few steam engines then were in a position to be able to use them, and it took a while for the list to grow. BR began to run steam excursions for itself when it found it could be a moneyspinning operation.

Then things went sour. There are too many tours, and rapidly rising hire-charges now seem almost to have stifled a goose which has laid a number of golden eggs. Many cancellations took place during the dry summer of 1995 (though not, it must be said, wholly because of high charges), and by the end of the year entire programmes had been suspended. Whether this market will recover remains to be seen, but if it does not there

Opposite BR Class 5MT 4-6-0 No. 73080 *Merlin* at work on the Mid-Hants Railway, July 3 1994 *(Mike Esau)*

14

will undoubtedly be some owners of large engines who will no longer be able to fund their maintenance. Some of the sites listed here will be poorer for this, and perhaps the longer lines may suffer a knock-on effect as the shortage of big engines begins to bite.

One has gained the impression over, say, the last ten years that the number of miniature railways – and so far as I am concerned this means anything less than 15in gauge, since by no stretch of the imagination can the Ravenglass or Romney lines be regarded as 'miniature' – has grown rapidly. But a great many of them have been about longer than might be supposed. The post-War boom is 40 years ago, after all. There have been new ones, it is true, but this writer's feeling is not so much that there are more of them, but that they are being marketed more imaginatively, reflecting the increased competition posed by other leisure activities. It is a commercial world, and sales forces ignore it at their peril, but one sincerely hopes that good taste will not degenerate into 'cheap and nastiness', since this could only react adversely on everyone else.

Two vital things govern the railway preservers' hobby – money and volunteers, and there is a shortage of both. Ways of acquiring the first have been both legion and ingenious. The Wine & Dine theme has been taken up in a number of places, and Santa Specials, Teddy Bears' Picnics, 'Thomas the Tank Engine' events, steam (and diesel) galas or events themed around a particular visiting locomotive all help to bring in the cash needed to keep things running. Locomotive driving courses are a more recent idea, and seem to be having success.

There are fewer expedients for solving the problem of the second. It is an aspect of the movement which saddens me personally that so few of our preserved schemes actually do anything to encourage the volunteers of the future, today's 12 to 15-year-olds. If there are going to be enough volunteers to run things in 25 years time – and even now one finds pleas for new recruits in practically every issue of the railway press – today's youngsters *must* be enthused. It is no use saying complacently, 'Oh the youngsters will come along when they're ready.' It's too late for that, and history already says that they haven't come. It is no good waiting until

they are 18 and then hoping for the best, for they will have other things to do by then, most of them. They must be caught and enthused long before that, and whatever one might think about the ethos of 'Thomas' weekends or Teddy Bears' Picnics, these are the times when a youngster is likely to be captured by the railway spirit.

Yet few attempt to foster this. I accept that the children are too young to work now, but why should that be a reason to ignore their potential? It is an ideal time to grab their imagination, and, having got it, work to hold it. I have, I confess, no statistics of the number of under-8s who attend 'Thomas' events up and down the country in the course of a year, but I would lay a fairly hefty wager that even if half of one per cent of the total was eligible to work, our labour problems would be over for up to 50 years.

Yes, there are problems – insurance, supervision, and other things too, but, given the will, these can and have been overcome by an enlightened few in Porthmadog, Alresford, Llanfair Caereinion and Sheffield Park. There are faint signs that others may be coming to a similar way of thinking, but it isn't (yet) anywhere near definite enough to hold your breath for! I have to say that my impression is not of resistance by management but, to put it bluntly, bloody-mindedness by the rank and file. If this really is the case it is very sad and very short-sighted. These youngsters are in no position to 'take their jobs from them', which is an argument one hears. They won't be for years, and one does wonder from where this apparent sense of insecurity arises. I suspect that reluctance to accept youngsters may rest less on anxiety about their own jobs than about concern for the reputation and future of the railway they love. This is wholly understandable, and very laudable, but it may also be sadly misguided. The new recruits have got to learn some time, and from someone – from whom if not them? Unless the youngsters are given a chance now there will be no-one to take over. Already some railways need paid staff to cover volunteer shortages. The bottom line of this is an increase in costs, affecting the railway's viability, and, in the end, whether it stays open or not. And how secure are jobs and the future of the railway they love then?

Opposite 4-6-2 No. 2 *Northern Chief*, built by Davey Paxman in 1925, on the 15in gauge Romney Hythe & Dymchurch Railway, June 1 1985 *(Mike Esau)*

Let it not be thought that I suggest in any way that the volunteers do not do a magnificent job. Of course they do – if they did not, I shouldn't be writing this Foreword, for there would be nothing to write about. And, as a volunteer myself, I have an interest, albeit a modest one. I have told elsewhere (*Awdry's Steam Railways*, Boxtree, 1995) of my travels round several lines during 1994, and if any proof of the volunteers' dedication had been needed it was amply illustrated everywhere I went.

A recent leader in *Steam Railway* reflected that the phrase: 'It can't be done, mate,' has re-echoed frequently through the years along the halls of preservation. How true. I've been hearing it ever since Tom Rolt took up the Talyllyn's cudgels in 1950, and I am quite prepared to admit I've said it myself, though it would be tactless to divulge what projects I said it about! The point, of course, is that the frontiers of preservation continue to be pushed forward again and again. Long may it be so, because only while there are the visionaries to do this can the movement survive. Perhaps our political leaders in both sides of the House may care to reflect on that.

Christopher Awdry
January 1996

Right LMS Class 3F 0-6-0T No. 47308 lets off steam on the Dean Forest Railway, September 11 1995 *(Mike Esau)*

The West Country and the Channel Islands

1. Alderney Railway Company
2. Alderney Miniature Railway
3. Avon Vale Railway
4. Beer Heights Light Railway
5. Bickington Steam Railway
6. Bicton Woodland Railway
7. Bodmin & Wenford Railway
8. Bristol Harbour Railway
9. Buckfastleigh Miniature Railway
10. Coate Water Park Miniature Railway
11. Crinkley Bottom Railway
12. Dean Forest Railway
13. East Somerset Railway
14. Exmoor Steam Centre
15. Gartell Light Railway
16. Gloucestershire Warwickshire Railway
17. Gorse Blossom Miniature Railway
18. Great Torrington Railway
19. Great Western Railway Museum (Swindon)
20. Great Western Railway Museum (Blue Anchor)
21. Great Western Railway Museum (Coleford)
22. Hunters Rest Miniature Railway
23. Lappa Valley Railway
24. Launceston Steam Railway
25. Lee Moor Tramway
26. Longleat Railway
27. Lynbarn Railway
28. Lynton & Barnstaple Railway Museum
29. Lynton & Barnstaple Railway Association
30. Manor Railways
31. Moors Valley Railway
32. National Waterways Museum
33. North Gloucestershire Railway
34. Paignton & Dartmouth Steam Railway
35. Pallot Heritage Steam Museum

36. Pecorama
37. Plym Valley Railway
38. Poole Park Railway
39. Rode Woodland Railway
40. Seaton & District Electric Tramway
41. Somerset & Avon Railway Association
42. Somerset & Dorset Railway Trust
43. Somerset & Dorset Railway Preservation Society
44. South Devon Railway
45. Swanage Railway
46. Swindon & Cricklade Railway
47. Tiverton Museum
48. Vobster Light Railway/Radstock Light Railway
49. West Bay Station Project
50. West Somerset Railway
51. Winchcombe Railway Museum
52. Woodspring Museum
53. Yeovil Country Railway

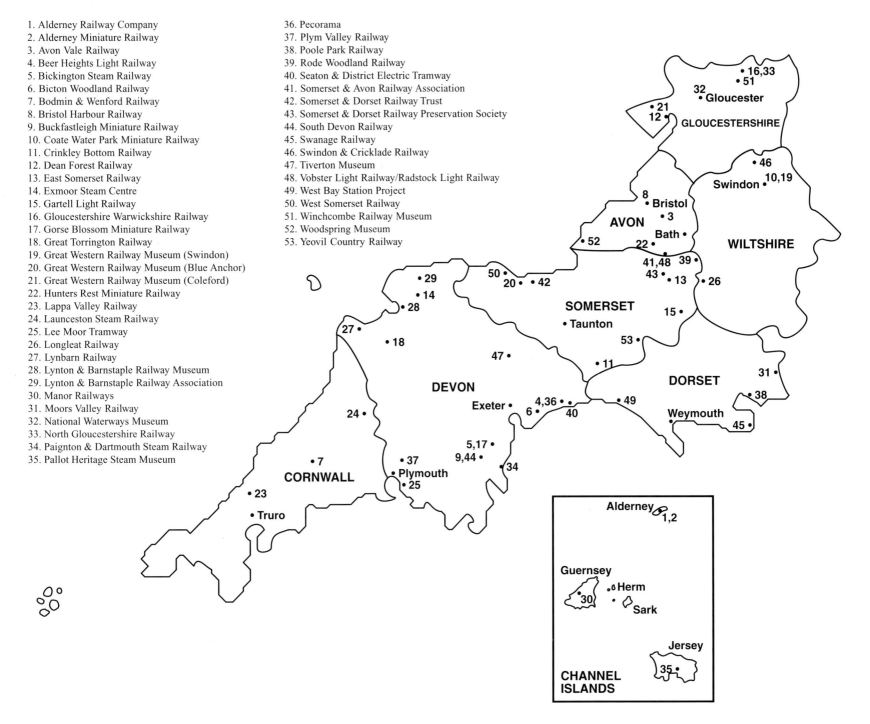

Alderney Railway Company

PO Box 75
Alderney
Channel Islands

Tel: 01481 823260
Route: Inner Harbour to Mannez Quarry
Length: 2 miles
Gauge: Standard
Open: Easter to end September on weekends and bank holidays, Santa Specials
Facilities: Shop at Braye Road and refreshments on Sundays

A short mineral line operated on the tiny island of Alderney from 1847 to 1984 linking the stone quarry to the breakwater. From 1980 the Alderney Railway Society leased the line from the Ministry of Defence and the first steam services started in 1982. Now trains are operated by a Vulcan Drewry 0-4-0 diesel, *Elizabeth*, and a Ruston 0-4-0 diesel, *Molly*, hauling two ex-London Underground cars dating from 1938, or by three Wickham Type 27 railcars.

Alderney Miniature Railway

Mannez Quarry
Alderney
Channel Islands

Route: Circuit within Mannez Quarry
Length: 1/4 mile
Gauge: 7 1/4 in
Open: When Alderney Railway is operating

This miniature railway is operated by Alderney Care Trust within the old stone quarry. Motive power is provided by green-liveried 7 1/4 in gauge 'Warship' class diesel locomotive, *HMS Alderney*. Passengers travel on sit-astride coaches and enjoy views of the island and its lighthouse.

Wickham trolleys wait for passengers at Braye Road station on the Alderney Railway *(Dr M A Taylor)*

Avon Vale Railway

Bitton Station
Willsbridge
Bristol BS15 6ED

Tel: 01272 327296 (talking timetable) or 0117 9325538 (weekends)
Route: Bitton to Oldland/Bitton to Fieldgrove
Length: 1 1/2 miles
Gauge: Standard
Open: Steam service - Easter to October on Sundays and bank holidays. Diesel service - May to September on Saturdays, June to August on Wednesdays. Santa Specials in December
Facilities: Shop, refreshments, car park, picnic site and coach with disabled facilities

The former Midland Railway route from Mangotsfield to Bath (Green Park) opened in 1869 and closed in 1966. It was used as part of a through route linking the Midlands and the North with Bournemouth via the Somerset & Dorset Joint Railway, route of the famous 'Pines Express'. The first open day was held at Bitton station by the Bristol Suburban Railway Society in 1983. First trains ran along the mile of line to Oldland in 1987. Oldland station opened in 1991 and in 1995 the first section from Bitton towards Bath (1/2 mile) was opened. Trains, either steam or diesel-hauled, currently run round at Fieldgrove where there are no station facilities.

Beer Heights Light Railway

Underleys
Beer
Nr Seaton
Devon EX12 3NA

Tel: 01297 21542
Route: Long return loop within grounds of
Pecorama (see p.36)
Length: 1 mile
Gauge: 7¼in
Open: Easter to end September, Autumn half
term. Telephone for details
Facilities: Licensed restaurant, car park,
children's activity areas, picnic area, model
railway exhibition (see Pecorama p.36)

Opened in 1975 by the Rev W Awdry, creator of
'Thomas the Tank Engine', this miniature railway
was built to complement the permanent Peco
Model Railway Exhibition. The railway has been
extended in stages and is widely regarded as one
of the most impressive 7¼in lines in the country.
In best Welsh narrow gauge tradition, the line is
built partly on a shelf on the hillside and follows
a circuitous route through deep cuttings and
embankments, over bridges and through a 180ft-
long tunnel. Four steam locomotives, including a
scale model of Festiniog Railway *Linda*, and one
diesel, all built to one-third full size, operate the
trains which give passengers superb views over
Lyme Bay.

Bickington Steam Railway

Trago Mills
Bickington
Newton Abbot
Devon

Tel: 01626 821111
Route: Around lakes within Trago Mills complex
Length: 1¼ miles
Gauge: 10¼in

Left A busy scene on the 7¼in gauge Beer Heights
Light Railway *(Beer Heights Light Railway)*

Open: Daily April to end October and weekends in Winter and school holidays, subject to weather. Closed Christmas week
Facilities: Car park, refreshments, shopping and leisure facilities, facilities for disabled

The miniature Bickington Steam Railway is situated at the famous Trago Mills Shopping and Leisure Centre. The railway opened in 1988 and originally comprised of two tracks, each of which was ³/₄ mile in length. During 1993 part of the inner circuit was lifted and used to extend the line to its current length. Trago Central is the main station, complete with ticket office, covered waiting area and two platforms linked by a footbridge. The railway incorporates a 23-pier viaduct, six bridges, three level crossings and a second station serving a Supakart track. On leaving the station trains encounter gradients of 1-in-49 as the line meanders through woodland, a nature reserve and around or across several lakes and streams, affording panoramic views of the Devonshire countryside. The railway is capable of operating up to four trains at any one time, being controlled by a three-aspect colour signalling system operated by four computers. The motive power for the railway is provided by four steam locomotives, *Blanche of Lancaster*, *E.R.Calthrop*, *Alice* and No. 24 *Sandy River*, and one diesel. Rolling stock comprises four sets of four articulated coaches, each set capable of carrying 50 passengers. The railway has a large workshop with storage facilities and a 20ft turntable.

Bicton Woodland Railway

Bicton Gardens
East Budleigh
Budleigh Salterton
Devon EX9 7DP

Tel: 01395 568465
Route: Within grounds of Bicton Park
Length: 1¹/₂ miles
Gauge: 18in
Open: Daily April to October, weekends November to March

2-6-4T *E R Calthrop* on the 10¹/₄in gauge Bickington Steam Railway *(Bickington Steam Railway)*

Facilities: Car park, shop, refreshments, museum, facilities for disabled

Completed in 1962 this narrow gauge line runs through the beautiful gardens, passing a lake and through woodland, in the grounds of Bicton Park. The 0-4-0 steam locomotive *Woolwich*, built by Avonside in 1916, and some of the rolling stock, date from World War I and originally worked on the Woolwich Arsenal Railway. Several other diesel locomotives and rolling stock originated from War Department and Air Ministry lines. Trains depart from Bicton Gardens station, skirting a lake before reaching Pine Junction where the line divides for a return loop through the gardens. A branch line runs alongside the lake to Hermitage Terminus. Plans for the future include a rebuilding programme for the carriages and a general revamp of the station buildings.

Bodmin & Wenford Railway

Bodmin General Station
Bodmin
Cornwall PL31 1AQ

Tel: 01208 73666
Route: Bodmin General to Bodmin Parkway (BR connection)
Length: 3¹/₂ miles
Gauge: Standard
Open: Easter to end October and Santa Specials in December. Telephone for details
Facilities: Car park (Bodmin), refreshments, shop and facilities for disabled

This line, the only standard gauge preserved railway in Cornwall, was originally the GWR branch from Bodmin Road to Boscarne Junction, opened in May 1887, which was closed to all traffic in November 1983. First passenger trains

23

ran in 1989 on the re-opened section from Bodmin General to Bodmin Parkway where there is an interchange with British Rail trains. An intermediate station at Colesloggett Halt gives passengers access to Cardinham Woods which has waymarked trails, cafe, picnic area and cycle hire facilities. Trains are mainly steam-hauled along this scenic line which includes gradients as steep as 1-in-37. Locomotives include five working industrial steam tanks and a former GWR 'Prairie', a 2-8-0 and an SR 'West Country' class 'Pacific' are being restored. A future extension along the mothballed line to Boscarne Junction is planned, with limited services scheduled to start in 1996, along with the re-opening of the 6½-mile freight-only china clay line to Wenford Bridge.

Bristol Harbour Railway

Bristol Industrial Museum
Princes Wharf
City Docks
Bristol BS1 4RN

Tel: 0117 9251470
Route: Along dockside between Museum and *SS Great Britain*
Length: ½ mile
Gauge: Standard
Open: Museum - Tuesday to Sunday all year
      Railway - Telephone for details
Facilities: Shop, facilities for disabled

The railway is part of the Bristol Industrial Museum which houses a large transport collection with excellent ship and railway models. The Bristol Harbour Railway originally opened to the quayside in 1866 and the present operation started in 1978. Steam trains operate on certain dates (telephone for details) along Princes and Wapping Wharves overlooking the floating harbour. The two restored steam locomotives,

Left GWR 0-6-0PT No. 7714 heads a charter freight on the Bodmin and Wenford Railway, July 15 1995 (Mike Esau)

that originally worked at Avonmouth Docks, are 0-6-0 saddle tanks No. 1764 *Portbury*, built by Avonside in 1917, and No. 1940 *Henbury*, built by Peckett in 1937. Passengers are carried in an open wagon and a GWR 'Toad' brake van. Future plans include possible extension of the line alongside the River Avon to 'A' Bond by the Cumberland Basin. The industrial museum also operates the restored steam tug *Mayflower* and a 35-ton steam crane, and Brunel's restored iron ship, *SS Great Britain*, is open to the public at the nearby Great Western Dry Dock.

Buckfastleigh Miniature Railway

Buckfastleigh Station
Buckfastleigh
Devon TQ11 0D2

Tel: 01364 42338
Route: Adjacent to South Devon Railway car park
Length: ¾ mile
Gauge: 7¼in
Open: Telephone for details
Facilities: Refreshments

This passenger-carrying miniature railway, situated adjacent to the South Devon Railway's car park at Buckfastleigh uses steam and internal combustion locomotives to haul its trains on a meandering route. Track was relaid using aluminium rail from Forest Railroad at Dobwalls.

Coate Water Park Miniature Railway

(North Wilts Model Engineers Society)
Coate Water Park
Swindon
Wilts

Tel: 01793 531117
Route: Within Coate Water Park
Length: 1,200yd
Gauge: 5in and 7¼in
Open: Sunday afternoons
Facilities: Club house

Operated by the North Wilts Model Engineers Society this dual-gauge miniature railway started life in 1961 on raised track. Rebuilt at ground level in 1966, it has been gradually extended over the years to its present layout of one outer circuit with an inner figure-of-eight. The line boasts a signalbox, signalling, a steaming bay and club house, and locomotives include a 5in gauge GWR 4-6-2 *Great Bear* and a Class 45 diesel. Passengers are carried on sit-on carriages based on a GWR design.

Crinkley Bottom Railway

Crinkley Bottom at Cricket St. Thomas
Estate Office
Cricket St. Thomas
Chard
Somerset TA20 4DD

Tel: 01460 30755
Route: Within wildlife park
Length: 900yd
Gauge: 15in
Open: Easter to end October. Telephone for details
Facilities: Normal facilities of leisure park, facilities for disabled

The Crinkley Bottom Railway is located in the paddock and woodland area near to a series of lakes in the wildlife park at Cricket St Thomas. The route is from Crinkley Bottom Junction to Crinkley Bottom station, near Mr Blobby's house, via the wildlife paddocks, woodland and a tunnel. The line was built in 1985 to take visitors from the northern to the southern end of the Park partly through an area not accessible on foot. The length of line was increased in 1986 when the station at the northern end was moved from the eastern side of the lakes to the western side and an iron bridge built to carry the line over the lake. In 1995, due to increased traffic demands, an extra passing loop was added to enable two trains to be run during busy periods. Two diesel locomotives operate the trains, the oldest dating back to 1957 when it was built for the Dudley Zoo railway, and the most recent supplied in 1995 by Alan Keef.

25

Both locomotives, which have the appearance of a garden shed on wheels, are capable of being driven from both ends of the train by the inclusion of a driving trailer unit. The partially enclosed carriages include accommodation for wheelchairs.

Dean Forest Railway

Norchard Railway Centre
Forest Road
Lydney
Glos GL15 4FT

Tel: 01594 843423 (talking timetable),
01594 845840
Route: Norchard to Lydney (near BR station)
Length: 2 miles

Gauge: Standard
Open: Daily for static viewing. Telephone for details of operating days
Facilities: Shop, refreshments, museum, riverside walks, picnic site, facilities for disabled

Steam trains now operate along this section of the old Severn & Wye Railway, originally a horse-drawn tramway, through the Forest of Dean. The line was last used by BR in 1976 and a preservation society first set up its base at Norchard in 1978, having been running steam open days at Parkend since 1972. The line was purchased from British Rail in 1985. Restored steam locomotives operating on the line include GWR 2-6-2 tank No. 5541, BR 0-6-0 pannier tank No. 9681 and three industrial steam engines. Trains currently run from Norchard to Lydney St

Above GWR 2-6-2T No. 5541 on the Dean Forest Railway, November 5 1994 *(Mike Esau)*

Mary's and Lydney Junction, where there is a footpath connection with BR. Future plans include extending the line two miles northwards from Norchard to Whitecroft and Parkend.

East Somerset Railway

Cranmore Station
Shepton Mallet
Somerset BA4 4QP

Tel: 01749 880417/01749 880785

Right BR Class 4MT 2-6-0 No. 76017 visited the East Somerset Railway in 1994 *(Julian Holland)*

Route: Merehead West to Cranmore to Mendip Vale
Length: 2³/₄ miles
Gauge: Standard
Open: Daily for static viewing. Telephone for details of 200 operating days
Facilities: Car park, refreshments, shop, art gallery, museum, picnic site, engine shed and workshops, facilities for disabled

One of only two steam-only lines in the country (the other being the Bluebell Railway) the East Somerset Railway was founded in 1973 by David Shepherd, the famous wildlife and railway artist, to provide a home for his steam locomotives which include BR Standard Class 4MT 4-6-0 No. 75029 *The Green Knight* and Class 9F 2-10-0 No. 92203 *Black Prince*. The two-road engine shed at Cranmore, built to a traditional GWR design, was opened in 1976. Trains presently operate from the attractive Cranmore station to Mendip Vale, on the outskirts of Shepton Mallet along part of the old GWR branch, affectionally known as 'The Strawberry Line', from Witham

Priory to Yatton, opened as a broad gauge route in 1858 and closed by BR in 1963. An extension eastwards to Merehead West may open in 1996. Occasional steam specials visit the railway from other parts of the system via the junction at Witham Priory on the main Westbury to Taunton line. GWR locomotives 0-4-2 tank No. 1450 and 4-6-0 *Nunney Castle*, owned by Riviera Trains, are now based at Cranmore from where they will haul main line steam specials.

Exmoor Steam Centre

Cape of Good Hope Farm
Nr Bratton Fleming
Barnstaple
N Devon EX32 7JN

Tel: 01598 710711
Route: Within farm site
Length: 1 mile
Gauge: 12¹/₄in
Open: Telephone for details
Facilities: Car park, picnic site, refreshments

Half actual size (6in to 1ft) narrow gauge steam locomotives carry passengers on a steeply-graded line giving fine views over Exmoor. The engines and rolling stock are built in the company's own workshop. Exmoor Town station is built in Victorian style and includes the refreshment area. A 2ft gauge South African Railways Garratt 2-6-2+2-6-2 No. NGG16.109 arrived at the Centre in 1995. This massive locomotive will be restored to working order for working over a short demonstration line.

Gartell Light Railway

Common Lane
Yenston
Nr Templecombe
Somerset BA8 0NB

Tel: 01963 370752
Route: Common Lane to Park Lane
Length: 1 mile
Gauge: 2ft
Open: Open May to September and Christmas on selected days only. Telephone for details of open days
Facilities: Car park, shop, refreshments, museum, lakeside picnic site, facilities for disabled

This superb narrow gauge line partly runs along the trackbed of the old Somerset & Dorset Joint Railway, closed in 1966, a mile south of Templecombe, and is run by three generations of the Gartell family. From small beginnings in 1982 the first public open day was held in 1990. Motive power is provided by five preserved industrial diesel locomotives and passengers can travel in either open-sided or covered bogie carriages. The line is fully signalled, using ex-BR equipment, and employs two fully operational signalboxes. The line is currently being extended northwards from Pinesway Junction along the S&D trackbed towards Templecombe, involving the construction of a flyover to take the extension over the existing line.

Left Open Day at Common Lane station on the Gartell Light Railway, July 1994 *(Julian Holland)*

Gloucestershire Warwickshire Railway

The Station
Toddington
Cheltenham
Glos GL54 5DT

Tel: 01242 621405
Route: Toddington to Far Stanley
Length: 5 miles
Gauge: Standard
Open: Weekends and bank holidays from March until mid October. Wednesdays and Thursdays in August. Santa Specials in December
Facilities: Car park, shop, refreshments, facilities for the disabled, 2ft gauge railway at Toddington (see North Gloucestershire Railway p.34)

The first stage of an eventual railway linking Broadway and Cheltenham along the former GWR main line from the Midlands to the South-West that was closed by BR in 1969. Trains currently run from Toddington to Far Stanley with an intermediate station at Winchcombe (originally the station building at Monmouth [Troy]). The railway owns the trackbed between Cheltenham and Broadway where there are possible future links further on with the existing BR system at Honeybourne. Future plans include re-opening the 1¹/₂ mile extension to Gotherington by 1997, to Cheltenham Racecourse by 2000 and to Broadway by 2005. Motive power is drawn from a fleet of eight steam and nine diesel locomotives and coaching stock consists of two rakes of ex-BR Mark 1 carriages, one set painted in chocolate and cream and the other in maroon. Visiting main line locomotives are a common sight on the railway. A journey along the line takes passengers through the picturesque North Gloucestershire countryside with fine views of the Cotswold escarpment, past Hailes Abbey to the beautifully restored station at Winchcombe (for Winchcombe Railway Museum see p.42), and then through the 693yd Greet tunnel to the present limit of the line at Far Stanley.

GWR 2-8-0 No. 2857, working on the Gloucestershire Warwickshire Railway *(Steve Standbridge)*

Gorse Blossom Miniature Railway

Liverton
Bickington
Newton Abbot
Devon TQ12 6JD

Tel: 01626 821361
Route: Within woodland park
Length: ³/₄ mile
Gauge: 7¹/₄in
Open: Daily end March to end October
Telephone for details
Facilities: Shop, refreshments, picnic site, car park, nature trails, model railway

The Gorse Blossom Railway was opened in July 1984 and overlooks the beautiful Teign Valley with views to Dartmoor. The 35-acre site was on redundant farm land and woodland which in the last century contained a quarry. The physical features of the land have provided the railway with plenty of scope for civil engineering features. The line is a continuous circuit served primarily by one station, Wellpark station, the line doubling back on itself to take advantage of the contours and includes high banks, deep hidden valleys, four tunnels, several bridges including a 48ft-long viaduct. Locomotives operating on the line include a ¹/₃rd scale Lynton & Barnstaple 2-6-2 tank, *Yeo*, a battery electric ¹/₅th scale Rhaetian Railway Bo-Bo *Klosters*, and a freelance petrol mechanical B-B *Pegasus*. A separate 7¹/₄in gauge miniature railway circuit with a battery electric locomotive is provided for children to drive themselves. Also featured is a 'G' scale outdoor model railway in a mountain setting based on the Albula line in Switzerland.

Great Torrington Railway

Mill Lodge
Town Mills
Great Torrington
Devon EX38 8PH

Tel: 01805 623328
Route: Out and back loop within wooded valley
Length: $1/2$ mile
Gauge: $7^1/_4$in
Open: Daily during Easter week and end May to mid September. Weekends only mid April to end May and mid to end September
Facilities: Car park, refreshments, shop, picnic site

The Great Torrington Railway is a miniature line situated next to the RHS Rosemoor Gardens. It was partially opened in 1990 and completed by Whitsun 1991. The route starts at a lower loop, near the car park, and climbs up through a narrow wooded valley to a small top return loop. Wild flowers and butterflies proliferate on this line, where gradients as steep as 1-in-45 are encountered. Trains are currently hauled by 0-4-2 coal-fired narrow gauge locomotive *Mark Rolle*, with two sit-astride cars and one covered car.

Great Western Railway Museum

Faringdon Road
Swindon
Wilts SN1 5BJ

Tel: 01793 493189
Open: Weekdays and Sunday afternoons all year
Closed Good Friday, Christmas Eve, Christmas Day and New Year's Day
Facilities: Souvenir shop

The museum is housed in a former lodging house for GWR workers which subsequently became a Methodist Chapel. The collection includes No. 6000 *King George V*, Dean Goods 0-6-0 No. 2516, 0-6-0 pannier tank No. 9400 and a replica of the broad gauge 2-2-2 *North Star*. Also on display are a large number of GWR photographs,

locomotive nameplates and other artefacts. Nearby a former railway worker's house has been restored to its original condition.

Great Western Railway Museum

Blue Anchor Station
Nr Minehead
West Somerset

Open: Sundays and bank holidays Easter to end September
Facilities: Car park

A small and interesting museum of GWR ephemera and artefacts housed in the old Great Western station building at Blue Anchor, which is situated on the West Somerset Railway (see p.41).

Great Western Railway Museum

The Old Railway Station
Railway Drive
Coleford
Glos GL16 8AZ

Tel: 01594 833569/832032
Open: Tuesday to Saturday afternoons Easter to end October , Saturdays afternoons only November to Easter
Facilities: Car park, shop, railway walk

The Great Western Railway Museum is housed in one of the last remaining railway buildings at the end of the Monmouth to Coleford branch line which opened in 1883 and closed to passengers in 1916 and goods in 1967. The former GWR signalbox from Cogload Junction, complete with working lever-frame, has been restored on the site. Exhibits, contained within the former GWR goods station, include Peckett 0-4-0 tank No. 1893, built in 1936, a GWR fruit van from 1911 and a six-wheeled LMS Brake Coach. Also displayed is a large collection of photographs of local railways, the Victorian ticket office, station master's office, railway artefacts and railway models ranging from gauge '00' to 5in. A $7^1/_4$in gauge miniature railway, due to be extended in

1996, operates on the site and trains are sometimes worked by 0-4-0 Bagnall saddle tank *Victor*.

Hunters Rest Miniature Railway

Hunters Rest Inn
King Lane
Clutton
Avon

Tel: 01761 452303
Route: Within grounds of public house
Length: $1/4$ mile
Gauge: 5in and $7^1/_4$in
Open: Weekends during summer months. Steam every Sunday afternoon in summer. Telephone for details
Facilities: Car park, refreshments during licensing hours

This dual-gauge miniature railway was built by the previous owner of this popular pub and expanded by the current owners. The figure-of-eight line runs through the landscaped pub gardens, past a lake and through a tunnel, and affords views across the Chew Valley to the Mendip Hills. Steam power is provided by a Hunslet $7^1/_4$in gauge tank locomotive.

Lappa Valley Railway

St. Newlyn East
Newquay
Cornwall TR8 5HZ

Tel: 01872 510317
Route: Benny Bridge Halt to East Wheal Rose Mine and Newlyn Downs Halt
Length: $1^1/2$ miles
Gauge: 15in and $10^1/_4$in
Open: Daily Easter to end October
Facilities: Car park, shop, refreshments, picnic area, historic mine, walks, miniature railways

This railway operates along part of the trackbed of the former GWR Chacewater to Newquay branch, opened in 1849 and closed by BR in

Above 0-6-4T No. 1 *Zebedee* on the 15in gauge Lappa Valley Railway *(N R Knight)*

1963. The 15in gauge line opened in 1974 and runs for one mile from Benny Halt to East Wheal Rose. The line includes a gradient of 1-in-100, a turntable at Benny and a large loop round a boating lake at East Wheal Rose. Locomotives operating the trains are 0-6-4 tank *Zebedee* and 0-6-0 tender engine *Muffin* plus one diesel and one petrol engine. A 10¼in gauge line was opened in 1995 and runs for ½ mile from East Wheal Rose to Newlyn Downs with a gradient of 1-in-70. Trains on this line are operated by petrol locomotive *Duke of Cornwall*. To complete the railway enthusiasts' small gauge day there is also a 7¼in gauge circuit at East Wheal Rose.

Launceston Steam Railway

St. Thomas Road
Newport
Launceston
Cornwall PL15 8DA

Tel: 01566 775665

Route: Launceston to New Mills
Length: 2½ miles
Gauge: 2ft
Open: Easter weekend, then Sundays and Tuesdays to Whitsun. Daily, excluding Saturdays, Whitsun to end September. Sundays and Tuesdays in October
Facilities: Museum, shop, refreshments, model railway, car park, picnic site, woodland walks, facilities for disabled

This narrow gauge line, opened in 1985, runs along part of the trackbed of the old London & South Western Railway's line from Halwill Junction to Padstow which closed in 1966. Locomotives, including *Lilian* and *Covertcoat*, built by Hunslet in 1883 and 1898 respectively, are beautifully restored steam engines that formerly worked in the North Wales slate quarries of Penrhyn and Dinorwic. Passengers are taken through the scenic Kensey Valley in replicas of Victorian narrow gauge carriages. The turn of the century workshop at Launceston is an example of

a belt-driven machine shop in daily use, and the British Engineering Exhibition gives an opportunity to view those locomotives not in service. Future plans include improvements to New Mills platform and Deer Park Halt.

Lee Moor Tramway

The Coach House
Saltram House
Plympton
Nr Plymouth
Devon

Tel: 01752 336546 (Main house)
Open: When Saltram House (National Trust) is open. Sunday to Thursday afternoons from April to end October
Facilities: Car park, refreshments, shop

Situated in the old coach house in the grounds of the National Trust property of Saltram House. The museum exhibits artefacts, a wagon and a locomotive from the now defunct 4ft 6in gauge Lee Moor Tramway, opened in 1854 to carry clay to Plymouth via the Cann Wood inclined plane, and finally closed in 1960. When the line closed, locomotives *Lee Moor No. 1* and *Lee Moor No. 2* were stored in Torycombe Engine Shed. Following restoration work on *Lee Moor No. 2*, by the Lee Moor Tramway Preservation Society, this locomotive was transferred to its current home at Saltram where it is now the centrepiece of the display. *Lee Moor No. 1* is now on display at the Wheal Martyn China Clay Museum near St. Austell.

Longleat Railway

Longleat House
Nr Warminster
Wilts

Tel: 01985 844579
Route: Alongside lake in grounds of Longleat House
Length: 1¼ miles
Gauge: 15in

Open: March to end October
Facilities: Car park, shop, refreshments, facilities for disabled

This line in the grounds of Longleat House was originally built in the 1960s and was resited in the 1970s. Passengers are taken on a return loop through woodland and alongside the lake, viewing deer, hippos, sea lions and gorillas. Motive power consists of one 0-6-2 steam locomotive, one 2-8-2 steam-outline diesel and one diesel railcar. Passengers are carried in a fleet of nine coaches, including one converted to carry wheelchairs.

Lynbarn Railway

The Milky Way
Downland Farm
Near Clovelly
North Devon

Tel: 01237 431255
Route: Within countryside centre
Length: 1/2 mile
Gauge: 2ft
Open: Daily April to October
Facilities: Car park, refreshments, family entertainments

The narrow gauge Lynbarn Railway is part of a large family entertainment complex and operates two steam-outline diesels with three bogie carriages. Kerr Stuart 0-6-0 tank No. 2451 *Axe*, built in 1915, is currently being restored to working order. Visitors to the Milky Way are given a free ride on the railway which is a fund-raising project operated by the Lynton & Barnstaple Railway Association (see below).

Lynton & Barnstaple Railway Museum

The Signal Box
Barnstaple Town Station
Castle Street
Barnstaple
N Devon

Tel: 01271 862930
Open: Monday to Saturday Easter to mid October

Housed in the former London & South Western Railway signalbox at the closed Barnstaple Town station, on the former Barnstaple Junction to Ilfracombe line, this museum depicts the history of the much-loved Lynton & Barnstaple narrow gauge railway which was closed by the Southern Railway in 1935. Exhibits include L&B artefacts and photographs.

Lynton & Barnstaple Railway Association

Woody Bay Station
Parracombe
North Devon EX31 4RA

Tel: 01271 862930
Open: Awaiting planning permission. Telephone for details
Facilities: None to date

The 1ft 11 1/2in narrow gauge Lynton & Barnstaple Railway was closed by the Southern Railway in 1935. After many years trying to re-open part of the line, the Lynton & Barnstaple Railway Association purchased the former Woody Bay station in 1995. Planning permission is being sought to open the station as a museum and to rebuild 3/4-mile of track. More future plans include re-opening a further 1/2-mile to Parracombe. It is hoped that the museum will be open in 1996, with trains operating in 1997.

Manor Railways

Sausmarez Manor
Sausmarez Road
St Martins
Guernsey
Channel Islands

Tel: 01481 38655
Route: Within grounds of manor house
Length: 1/4 mile

Gauge: 7 1/4in
Open: Daily
Facilities: Car park, refreshments, large model railway

Built in 1987 by the owners this miniature railway was extended to its present layout in 1990. Trains run on a curving route through woodland and are hauled by either 0-4-0 narrow gauge steam loco *Romulus* or a Class 25 diesel. There is also a large '00' gauge exhibition layout covering 350sq ft in a 16th century Tudor Barn and self-drive 'G' scale trains in the garden.

Moors Valley Railway

Moors Valley Country Park
Horton Road
Ashley Heath
Nr Ringwood
Dorset BH24 2ET

Tel: 01425 471415
Route: Within Moors Valley Country Park
Length: 1 mile
Gauge: 7 1/4in
Open: Daily Spring bank holiday to mid September and all school holidays. Weekends March to end October. Sundays November to end February
Facilities: Car park, shop, refreshments, picnic sites, adventure playground, forest walks

Established in 1986 the Moors Valley Railway operates a large collection of ten miniature steam locomotives and 57 pieces of rolling stock. More locomotives are planned for the future including a 2-4-0+0-4-2 Garratt type. This professionally-run railway includes four tunnels, signalbox, signalling and a roundhouse, and the journey around a lake takes in a spiral, steep gradients and tight curves.

Opposite Driver's-eye view of the Launceston Steam Railway (*AA Photo Library*)

National Waterways Museum

Llanthony Warehouse
Gloucester Docks
Gloucester GL1 2EH

Tel: 01452 318054
Open: Daily except Christmas Day
Facilities: Car park, refreshments, shop, facilities
for disabled

The museum tells the story of 200 years of inland
waterways on three floors of a former Victorian
warehouse in Gloucester Docks, and includes two
quaysides of floating exhibits, railway wagons
and unique working wagon turntables. Restored
railway rolling stock includes seven goods
wagons and a steam-operated crane.

North Gloucestershire Railway Company

The Station
Toddington
Cheltenham
Glos GL54 5DT

Tel: 01452 539062
Route: Alongside Gloucestershire Warwickshire
Railway line at Toddington (see p. 29)
Length: 1/2 mile
Gauge: 2ft
Open: Sunday and bank holiday afternoons Easter
to September
Facilities: Car park, train rides, engine shed,
museum

A steam-operated narrow gauge line within the
station limits at Toddington and alongside the
Gloucestershire Warwickshire Railway line at a
lower level. It was formed in 1985 to replace the
Dowty Railway Preservation Society that was based
at Ashchurch from 1962, all stock being moved to
the present site in 1983. Train services commenced
in 1990 and the railway now owns ten steam and
diesel narrow gauge locomotives, including
examples from Germany and South Africa. Track
used on the line came from the Southend Pier

Wagon restoration at the National Waterways Museum, Gloucester *(National Waterways Museum)*

Railway and former War Department
installations. The three coaches currently in use
were all constructed by the company, using
unsprung ex-WD wagon frames. Also of interest
are the signals which came from branch lines in
and around Gloucestershire and the former
Midland Railway signalbox, built in 1920, which
was previously situated at California Crossing in
Gloucester. Future plans include a possible
1/3-mile extension of the line to Didbrook Bridge.

Paignton & Dartmouth Steam Railway

Queen's Park Station
Paignton
Devon TQ4 6AF

Tel: 01803 555872
Route: Paignton Queen's Park to Kingswear
Length: 7 miles
Gauge: Standard
Open: Easter to October and Santa Specials in
December

Facilities: Car parks, refreshments, shop, Rail &
River Cruises, Wine & Dine train, facilities for
disabled

Preserved as a typical GWR seaside branch line
the Paignton & Dartmouth Steam Railway has a
fascinating history. A broad gauge line from
Torquay was built by the Dartmouth & Torbay
Railway Company, reaching Paignton in 1859
and Churston in 1861. A branch to Brixham was
opened in 1867. Although originally intending to
bridge the Dart to reach Dartmouth, the railway
was finally terminated at Kingswear in 1864,
being converted to standard gauge by the Great
Western Railway in 1892. Scheduled for closure
by British Rail in 1972 (the Brixham branch
having succumbed in 1963) the line was taken
over by the Dart Valley Light Railway Ltd in the
same year. Services began in 1973 and were
worked by this company until 1991. Since then
the operating company has been the Paignton &
Dartmouth Steam Railway and it has the

Right GWR 2-6-2T No. 4588 on the Paignton &
Dartmouth Steam Railway *(AA Photo Library)*

advantage of being linked with the national system at Paignton. At the other end of the line, Kingswear, passengers from the trains can take a ferry across the River Dart to Dartmouth. A journey along the line offers a variety of scenic attractions including three viaducts and a tunnel, passing sandy beaches and a river estuary. Ex-GWR steam locomotives and three ex-BR diesel trains run regular services along this attractive route, with an ex-'Devon Belle' observation car being attached to certain trains. Coaching stock comprises 20 ex-BR Mark 1 coaches. The 'Riviera Belle' dining train is also provided on certain evenings and for Sunday lunches (please telephone for details).

Pallot Heritage Steam Museum

Trinity
Jersey
Channel Islands

Open: April to October
Facilities: Shop, facilities for disabled

A museum, opened in 1990, devoted to the age of steam includes a private collection of industrial, agricultural and railway exhibits. A newly-built Victorian style station and engine shed, loosely styled on the Jersey Eastern Railway terminus at Snow Hill, St Helier, have been built, and it is intended to operate trains on both standard gauge and 2ft gauge track. Included in the collection are four standard gauge steam tank locomotives, two North London Railway coaches, a Jersey Eastern Railway brake van and passenger coach, and part of a JER Sentinel-Cammell railcar. 2ft gauge stock includes a Simplex diesel, carriages and brake van. The Jersey Light Railway Society hopes to reinstate the Jersey Railways & Tramways line from St Helier to Corbiere.

Pecorama

Underleys
Beer
Nr Seaton
Devon EX12 3NA

Tel: 01297 21542
Open: Easter to October. Telephone for details
Facilities: See Beer Heights Light Railway (p.22)

An exhibition of model railways in many different scales and gauges showing how they can be designed and located to fit into many different parts of the house or in the garden. A small display of railway relics and paraphernalia is also displayed. Former 'Golden Arrow' Pullman Car Orion stands on a short standard gauge length of track and now serves as a wine bar. The adjacent Beer Heights Light Railway (see p.22) is also part of the Pecorama complex.

Plym Valley Railway

Marsh Mills Station
Plymouth
Devon PL7 4NL

Route: Marsh Mills to Plym Bridge
Length: 1/2 mile
Gauge: Standard
Open: Sundays and bank holidays
Facilities: Shop and refreshments

Work is in progress to re-open part of the former Great Western Railway's route from Plymouth to Tavistock that was closed by BR in 1962. At present the short section from Marsh Mills to Plym Bridge is being restored. Fully operational locomotives working on the line include ex-Falmouth Docks 0-4-0 saddle tank No.3, ex-BR Class 08 0-6-0 diesel No. 13002 (the oldest working Class 08 diesel shunter in the country) and an ex-BR Class 117 diesel multiple unit. Ex-BR Class 4MT 4-6-0 No. 75079 is currently being restored.

Poole Park Railway

Poole Park
Poole
Dorset

Tel: 01202 683701 (evenings)

Route: Within Poole Park
Length: 1/2 mile
Gauge: 101/4in
Open: Afternoons daily from April to end October, mornings also in school holidays. Weekend afternoons in Winter subject to weather conditions
Facilities: Refreshments all year except Christmas, boating, crazy golf and tennis in summer

This miniature railway started life as Southern Miniature Railways in 1949 and was one of a number of similar railways owned by the same company at Stokes Bay, Bognor Regis and Southsea. The line was originally constructed and operated by George Vimpany until 1979 when a new partnership took over. The route of the line is circular around the perimeter of a wildfowl lake within the park, and possesses a basic station building and engine shed. Locomotives operating the line include 0-6-0 saddle tank *Arthur* and an Intercity diesel. At present there are plans to build another station and extend the line, and with this in mind the present owner has purchased equipment from the Royal Victoria Park Railway.

Rode Woodland Railway

Rode Bird Gardens
Rode
Nr Bath
Somerset BA3 6QW

Tel: 01373 830326
Route: Within grounds of Rode Bird Gardens
Length: 2/3 mile
Gauge: 71/4in
Open: Daily Easter to end September, weekends February half term to Easter and mid September to Autumn half term
Facilities: Car park, refreshments, shop, facilities for disabled, picnic sites, special miniature railway weekends (telephone for details)

Right Hawthorn Leslie 0-4-0ST No. 3, built in 1926, on the Plym Valley Railway, May 30 1994 *(B Mills)*

This steeply-graded miniature railway at the 17-acre Rode Bird Gardens opened in 1988 and runs through woodland, the pheasantries and pets corner, and employs two 0-6-0 saddle tanks and an 0-4-2 steam locomotive. Rolling stock comprises 13 four-seater sit-in coaches. Future plans include completion of the signalling system. Special miniature railway weekends, when many visiting locomotives can be seen operating, are held at several times through the year.

Seaton & District Electric Tramway

Riverside Depot
Harbour Road
Seaton
Devon EX12 2NQ

Tel: 01297 21702/20375
Route: Seaton to Colyton
Length: 3 miles
Gauge: 2ft 9in
Open: Easter to end September, Monday to Friday in October
Facilities: Refreshments, facilities for disabled

Originally opened in 1868 as a standard gauge branch from Seaton Junction, on the main line from Salisbury to Exeter, to Seaton. It was taken over by the London & South Western Railway in 1885 and eventually closed by BR in 1966. In 1969 Modern Electric Tramways of Eastbourne took over the trackbed and stock was moved to Seaton in 1970. The present 2ft 9in gauge line from Seaton to Colyton was finally completed in 1980 and now miniature replica electric trams, taking their power from overhead wires, take passengers on a delightful trip firstly alongside the estuary of the River Axe and then, at Colyford station, along the valley of the River Coly to the present terminus at Colyton. The fleet consists of five open-top double-deck trams, two enclosed trams, one toast-rack for disabled people and one illuminated tram for evening operating. A new Victorian tram-style terminus at Seaton was opened in 1995.

Somerset & Avon Railway Association

Radstock
Nr Bath
Avon

Open: Weekends

A scheme that is still in its embryo stage to re-open the former GWR line from Radstock to Frome. Opened in 1854 to tap the coalfields of north Somerset the line was eventually extended to Bristol, the latter section opening in 1873. The complete route was taken over by the GWR in 1884 and closed to passengers by BR in 1959. Freight continued to run for some years but, with the closure of the last coal mine at Writhlington in 1973 the remaining part of the line from Radstock to Frome was reduced to serving the Marcroft wagon repair works at Radstock. This has since closed leaving the short section from Frome to Somerset Quarry Junction, near Mells Road, open for stone trains from ARC's Whatley Quarry. However all the track is still in situ, if a little overgrown, and vehicle restoration work is currently progressing at Radstock. Future progress depends on the financial support of the local authorities. For further information about this project please contact Les Poolman, Membership Secretary, 25 Wells Square, Radstock, Avon BA3 3UF. Also based at Radstock, where it is being rebuilt, is the narrow gauge Vobster Light Railway/Radstock Light Railway (see p.41).

Somerset & Dorset Railway Trust

Washford Station
Watchet
Somerset TA23 0PP

Tel: 01984 640869
Open: When West Somerset Railway is operating (see p. 41)
Facilities: Shop, museum

Originally situated at Radstock, the museum moved to its present site in 1975-6. Situated in Washford Station on the West Somerset Railway (see p.41) the Somerset & Dorset Railway Trust Museum contains artefacts and archive material primarily, but not exclusively, from the S&DJR. These include a replica of the Midford signalbox and the actual signalbox from Burnham-on-Sea. In the goods yard opposite the station there is 1/4-mile of track with a display of restored locomotives and rolling stock. Former S&DJR 2-8-0 No. 88, owned by the Trust, is currently operating on the adjoining West Somerset Railway. Three former S&DJR six-wheeled coaches are under restoration, together with Hawthorn Leslie 0-6-0 saddle tank *Isabel*.

Somerset & Dorset Railway Restoration Society

c/o 40 Belvedere
Lansdowne Road
Bath BA1 5HR

Tel: 01225 448448
A new scheme to re-open ten miles of this famous and unique cross-country main line, closed in 1966, from Radstock over the legendary seven-mile climb to Masbury Summit and the outskirts of Shepton Mallet. The first five-year plan needs to raise £750,000 to purchase and reclaim buildings, trackbed, rails, rolling stock and build new bridges. The Society hopes to have at least a three-mile line operating by 2000.

South Devon Railway

Buckfastleigh Station
Buckfastleigh
Devon TQ11 OD2

Tel: 01364 642338
Route: Buckfastleigh to Totnes (Littlehempston)
Length: 7 miles
Gauge: Standard
Open: April to October, Santa Specials in December. Telephone for details

Right GWR 0-4-2T No. 1466 and autocar on the South Devon Railway, October 13 1995 *(Mike Esau)*

high charges made by the state operator for this privilege the practice was abandoned. In 1990 the South Devon Railway Trust took over the running of the railway and this change of ownership has been a great success. One of the highlights of recent years has been the opening of the South Devon Railway station at Totnes (Littlehempston) which is connected via a footbridge over the River Dart to the car park of the nearby BR station. Trains are currently mainly steam-hauled and rolling stock includes superbly restored vintage GWR carriages which are available for hire on special occasions. River-Rail cruises are also available using the South Devon Railway to Totnes followed by a cruise down the River Dart to Dartmouth. A railway museum, adjoining Buckfastleigh station, contains many fascinating railway artefacts and relics, including London & South Western Railway 2-4-0 Beattie well tank No. 0298 and broad gauge South Devon Railway 0-4-0 vertical-boilered locomotive *Tiny*, built in 1868.

Swanage Railway

Station House
Railway Station
Swanage
Dorset BH19 1HB

Tel: 01929 425800/01929 424276 (talking timetable)
Route: Swanage to Norden
Length: 6 miles
Gauge: Standard
Open: Weekends mid February to end December, daily May to October
Facilities: Shop, refreshments, picnic site, narrow gauge railway, museum, facilities for disabled, Wine & Dine trains, park-and-ride from Norden

The former London & South Western Railway branch line on the Isle of Purbeck was opened from Worgret Junction, a mile west of Wareham, to Swanage in 1885. The opening of the line changed Swanage from a small harbour town to a thriving seaside resort. Goods traffic was also

LNER Class A3 4-6-2 No. 60103 *Flying Scotsman* visited the Swanage Railway in 1994 *(Julian Holland)*

Facilities: Shop, refreshments, car parks, museum, picnic site, facilities for disabled, miniature railway (see Buckfastleigh Miniature Railway p.25)

Originally opened as a broad gauge railway in 1872, converted to standard gauge by the GWR in 1892, and closed by BR in 1962 the South Devon Railway evokes all the atmosphere of a sleepy GWR West Country branch line as it follows the

winding valley of the River Dart. One of the earliest preserved lines it was re-opened in 1969 and was eventually jointly operated with its seaside cousin, the Paignton & Dartmouth, by the Dart Valley Light Railway Ltd. One of the main drawbacks to the success of the preserved railway was the lack of access for passengers at the Totnes end of the line. For a short period between 1985 and 1988 Dart Valley trains were able to run into the BR station at Totnes but due partly to the important with large amounts of clay being carried from the Furzebrook area. Passenger traffic was heavy, especially during the summer months and included through carriages from Waterloo. The line was controversially closed by BR in 1972 although the section from Worgret Junction to the Wytch Farm oil terminal was retained. A preservation group started to re-open the line from Swanage and first trains ran along a short section from the station in 1979. By August 1995 the line had been extended to Corfe Castle and Norden, and on its first week of extended operation packed trains carried over 20,000 passengers. A park-and-ride scheme is in operation from Norden which should help to ease road traffic congestion in the Corfe Castle and Swanage areas. The railway is now planning to extend to Worgret Junction and Wareham, where it will connect with the national system. Trains are mainly steam-hauled by a variety of locomotives, and the 'Wessex Belle' Pullman dining train service is operated on certain Saturday evenings. Locomotives operating on the line include Southern Railway 'Battle of Britain' class 4-6-2 No. 34072 *257 Squadron* and Class M7 0-4-4 tank No. 30053. Visiting locomotives can frequently be seen, the highlight in recent years being the visit of *Flying Scotsman* in 1994.

Swindon & Cricklade Railway

Blunsdon Station
Blunsdon
Swindon
Wilts SN2 4DZ

Tel: 01793 771615 (weekends only)
Route: Within Blunsdon station area
Length: 1 mile
Gauge: Standard
Open: Weekends only. Telephone for details
Facilities: Shop, refreshments, museum coach, car park

Situated on the former Midland & South Western Junction Railway between Cheltenham Spa (St James) and Swindon, Blunsdon station was itself closed in 1937 and the line closed by BR in the early 1960s. A preservation group took over the station area in 1979 and now provides mainly steam-hauled trains along a short section of reinstated track. Future plans include a four-mile extension of the line towards Cricklade.

Tiverton Museum

St. Andrew Street
Tiverton
Devon EX16 6PH

Tel: 01884 256295
Open: Daily except Sundays and Christmas
Facilities: Shop

The main showpiece of this local West Country museum is GWR 0-4-2T No. 1442, affectionately known as the 'Tivvy Bumper', situated in a purpose-built railway gallery and surrounded by many exhibits and photographs of the golden age of steam trains on the Exe Valley line. The gallery has a fine collection of railway memorabilia including some trackway from Brunel's original broad gauge line, along with many GWR exhibits showing the local railway system in operation over the years.

Vobster Light Railway/Radstock Light Railway

Radstock
Nr Bath
Avon

Route: Within site of Somerset & Avon Railway at Radstock (see p. 38)
Gauge: 2ft
Length: ¼ mile
Open: Static viewing on Sundays

Until recently this 2ft gauge line ran for a short distance on trackbed of the former colliery line from Mells Road. Built in the 1860s to Brunel's broad gauge, this was rebuilt to standard gauge in 1874 and finally closed in 1965. The project to build a narrow gauge line was launched in 1991 and construction started in 1992. Open days were held at Holwell Farm but the complete railway has recently been resited at Radstock, adjacent to the Somerset & Avon Railway Association's operation (see p.38). Motive power consists of a collection of historic industrial diesel and petrol-engined locomotives, some in restored condition. Items of industrial narrow gauge rolling stock, acquired from many locations, are supplemented by the air-braked bogie passenger coach completed in 1992 for use on the railway.

West Bay Station Project

West Bay
Bridport
Dorset

Open: Daily

West Bay station, the terminus of the former GWR branch line from Maiden Newton, has been fully restored. A short length of track within the station site is now home to two railway carriages. Plans have recently been announced to build a narrow gauge railway linking West Bay with Bridport. For details telephone 01308 427345.

West Somerset Railway

The Railway Station
Minehead
Somerset TA24 5BG

Tel: 01643 704996/01643 707650 (talking timetable)
Route: Minehead to Bishop's Lydeard
Length: 20 miles
Gauge: Standard
Open: March to October and Sundays in November. Santa Specials in December. Telephone for details
Facilities: Refreshments, shop, Wine & Dine trains, car parking, museums, facilities for disabled

Britain's longest preserved railway, running past the rolling Quantock Hills to the sea, was

Left GWR '5101' class 2-6-2T No. 4160 on the West Somerset Railway *(West Somerset Railway)*

originally opened as a broad gauge line from Norton Fitzwarren, on the main Taunton to Exeter line, to Watchet in 1862 and extended to Minehead in 1874. The line was initially operated by the Bristol & Exeter Railway and then by its successor, the Great Western Railway, who converted it to standard gauge in 1882. Although the opening of Butlin's holiday camp at Minehead in 1962 brought an increase in traffic the line was eventually closed by BR in 1971. It was partly re-opened, from Minehead to Williton, in 1976 by the newly formed West Somerset Railway Company, who leased the line from Somerset County Council. By 1979 the line had been extended to its present terminus at Bishop's Lydeard. The section from here to Norton Fitzwarren is not currently used on a regular basis but there is a physical connection with BR with a very limited number of through trains being run from the national system on to the WSR. Plans to run a regular service to Taunton have been obstructed for many years, originally by opposition from the National Union of Railwaymen and then by official BR bureaucracy. A bus service links Bishop's Lydeard with Taunton. The present West Somerset Railway is home to a variety of steam and diesel locomotives (the diesel preservation group being based at Williton) as well as the GWR museum at Blue Anchor (see p.30) and the Somerset & Dorset Trust's museum at Washford (see p.38). Steam

locomotives include S&DJR Class 7F 2-8-0 No. 88, GWR '2251' class 0-6-0 No. 3205 and GWR 'Manor' class 4-6-0 No. 7820 *Dinmore Manor*. Visiting locomotives can regularly be seen at work on the line. The ten picturesque stations on the line have all been painstakingly preserved and a journey evokes all the atmosphere of a GWR country railway. Future plans, include improvements to Minehead locomotive shed and Bishop's Lydeard station, and a new diesel depot for Williton.

Winchcombe Railway Museum

23 Gloucester Street
Winchcombe
Gloucestershire

Tel: 01242 620641
Open: Daily in August, weekends and bank holidays Easter to October
Facilities: Shop, refreshments

A hands-on museum of railway life, situated near the Gloucestershire Warwickshire Railway (see p.29), featuring many visitor-operated exhibits. The collection was established in 1962 and is now operated by a voluntarily run Trust. The current major project is the conservation of the only surviving World War I London & North Western Railway ambulance train carriage body.

Woodspring Museum

Burlington Street
Weston-super-Mare
Avon BS23 1PR

Tel: 01934 621028
Open: Tuesdays to Sundays
Facilities: Refreshments and education room

Woodspring museum serves to collect and display the human and natural history of Woodspring. This area included part of Brunel's Bristol & Exeter Railway, the Cheddar Valley Railway, and the Wrington Vale Light Railway. The display also includes exhibits from the quaint Weston, Clevedon & Portishead Light Railway that was operated by the legendary Colonel H F Stephens and closed in 1940.

Yeovil Country Railway

Yeovil Junction Station
Nr Yeovil
Somerset

Route: Over part of former Clifton Maybank spur at Yeovil Junction
Length: 1/4 mile
Gauge: Standard
Open: See press for details
Facilities: Car park and refreshments at Yeovil Junction station

This short line was opened in November 1995 and a full programme of events is planned for 1996. The route is from the former down platform at Yeovil Junction and along part of the Clifton Maybank spur which closed over 60 years ago. Motive power currently consists of Peckett 0-4-0 saddle tank *Pectin*, with passengers conveyed in a brakevan. The locomotive turntable at Yeovil Junction is also leased from Railtrack by the railway's company, South West Main Line Steam Company.

South and South East England

1. Amberley Museum
2. Bentley Miniature Railway
3. Bluebell Railway
4. Buckinghamshire Railway Centre
5. Chinnor & Princes Risborough Railway
6. Cholsey & Wallingford Railway
7. Colonel Stephens Museum
8. Didcot Railway Centre
9. Drusillas Zoo Park Railway
10. Eastbourne Miniature Steam Railway
11. Eastleigh Lakeside Railway
12. East Herts Miniature Railway
13. East Kent Light Railway
14. Elham Valley Line Trust
15. Great Bush Railway
16. Great Cockrow Railway
17. Great Whipsnade Railway
18. Hollycombe Steam Collection
19. Hythe Pier Railway
20. Isle of Wight Steam Railway
21. Kent & East Sussex Railway
22. Kew Bridge Steam Museum
23. Knebworth Miniature Railway
24. Lavender Line
25. Leighton Buzzard Railway
26. London Toy & Model Museum
27. London Transport Museum
28. Mid-Hants Railway
29. Mizens Railway
30. Norton Ash Railway
31. Old Kiln Agricultural Museum
32. Pendon Museum
33. Polytechnic Stadium Railway
34. Queen Mary's Railway
35. Romney Hythe & Dymchurch Railway
36. Romsey Signal Box Project
37. Royal Victoria Railway
38. Ruislip Lido Railway
39. Science Museum
40. Sittingbourne & Kemsley Railway
41. Southall Railway Centre
42. Spa Valley Railway
43. Swanley New Barn Railway
44. Syon Park Miniature Railway
45. Thames Ditton Miniature Railway
46. Vanstone Woodland Railway
47. Volks Electric Railway
48. Watford Miniature Railway
49. Wellington Country Park Miniature Railway
50. Willen Miniature Railway
51. Yafford Mill & Farm Museum

43

7¼in gauge 4-6-0 No. 44804 at work on the Bentley Miniature Railway *(Bentley Miniature Railway)*

Amberley Museum

Houghton Bridge
Amberley
Arundel
West Sussex BN18 9LT

Tel: 01798 831370
Open: Wednesday to Sunday, bank holiday
Mondays from late March to early November.
Daily mid July to early September
Facilities: Shop, refreshments, picnic site,
museum, audio-visual display

The Narrow Gauge & Industrial Railway
Collection, part of a larger industrial museum, is
set in an old chalk pit near to the BR station at
Amberley. Exhibits include a large collection of
narrow gauge steam and diesel industrial
locomotives from Britain and abroad, including
former Groudle Glen 2-4-0 tank *Polar Bear* built
by Bagnall in 1905 and Bagnall 0-4-0 saddle tank
Peter built in 1918. The railway consists of 500yd
of passenger line and a complex of industrial
lines over which works and demonstration trains
are run. The 2ft gauge passenger-carrying line
operates steam trains most Sundays and bank
holiday Mondays and an annual railway gala is
held in late June. Historic passenger rolling stock
consists of an ex-RAF Hudson bogie coach, two
Penrhyn Quarrymen's coaches and three Groudle
Glen four-wheeled coaches.

Bentley Miniature Railway

Bentley Wildfowl & Motor Museum
Halland
Nr Lewes
East Sussex

Tel: 01825 840573
Route: In the grounds of the Bentley Wildfowl
Park
Length: ½ mile
Gauge: 5in and 7¼in
Open: Sundays and bank holidays Easter to end
September, Wednesdays and Saturdays in August
Facilities: Car park, refreshments, picnic site,
facilities for disabled

A mixed gauge passenger-carrying miniature
railway operated by Uckfield Model Railway
Club. First built in 1985 to a small circuit of 600ft
but recently extended to give a ½-mile run, the
ground-level line runs beside fields and
woodland, and includes a deep cutting, three
bridges and a 30ft tunnel. Two stations are
situated on the line, one near the picnic area and
the other at the edge of Glyndebourne Wood.
Locomotives operating on the line range from
small narrow gauge engines to a 'Britannia' class
4-6-2 and are all owned by club members.
Rolling stock is sit-astride bogie types.

Bluebell Railway

Sheffield Park Station
Nr Uckfield
East Sussex TN22 3QL

Tel: 01825 723777/01825 722370 (talking
timetable)
Route: Sheffield Park to Kingscote
Length: 9½ miles
Gauge: Standard
Open: Daily May to September half term holidays
and weekends all year. Santa Specials in
December
Facilities: Shops, refreshments, car parks, picnic
site, Wine & Dine train, museum, facilities for
disabled

The Bluebell Railway is the second oldest
standard gauge preserved line in Britain (the
Middleton Railway in Leeds having beaten it by
only two months), having celebrated its 35th
anniversary in 1995, and is also one of only two
standard gauge steam-only lines in the country
(the other being the East Somerset Railway, see
p.26). Opened in 1883 as part of the Lewes &
East Grinstead Railway, subsequently taken over

Right SECR 'C' class 0-6-0 No. 592, built in 1901,
on the Bluebell Railway, April 9 1995 *(Mike Esau)*

by the London Brighton & South Coast Railway, the line was a rural through route linking East Grinstead and Lewes. After two Enquiries BR closed the line in 1955. However it was soon discovered that the closure was illegal and services re-commenced in 1956 with final closure following in 1958. The Bluebell Railway Preservation Society was founded in 1959, and services started between Horsted Keynes and Sheffield Park in 1960. Although originally linked to the national system via the electrified Haywards Heath to Horsted Keynes branch, this connection was severed in 1963 when that line was closed. The extension to Kingscote through West Hoathly tunnel was opened in 1994. Work is now in progress to extend the line across the spectacular Mill Place viaduct from Kingscote to East Grinstead, hopefully by 2000, where it will make an important link again with the national network. Trains run by beautifully restored steam locomotives and vintage carriages presently terminate at Kingscote, two miles short of the railway's eventual northern terminus. Locomotives include examples from the LBSCR,

SECR, LSWR, NLR, GWR, SR and BR, the oldest being LBSCR Class A1X 0-6-0T No. 72 *Fenchurch* built in 1872, and the youngest being BR Class 9F 2-10-0 No. 92240 built in 1959. The Bluebell Railway is widely used by film and TV companies seeking authentic period locations, and this in turn has led to a great public awareness of the line.

Buckinghamshire Railway Centre

Quainton Railway Station
Nr Aylesbury
Bucks HP22 4BY

Tel: 01296 655720/01296 655450 (talking timetable)
Route: Within site
Length: 1/2 mile
Gauge: Standard
Open: Sundays and bank holiday Mondays Easter to October
Facilities: Car park, shop, refreshments, museum, miniature railway, picnic site, steam driving courses, facilities for disabled

A 25-acre railway centre incorporating two demonstration lines based on the former Metropolitan Railway country station at Quainton Road, where that railway originally met the Great Central Railway. The centre, opened in 1969, houses a very large collection of steam and diesel locomotives which operate trains along two short sections of track within the site. Occasional specials also work from Quainton Road to Aylesbury Town along the goods-only line still operated by Railtrack. Both engines and rolling stock are restored to working order in well-equipped workshops which are open to public viewing. Locomotives and rolling stock include Metropolitan Railway 0-4-4T No. 1, London & South Western Railway 2-4-0 well tank No. 0314, ex-GWR/London Transport 0-6-0 pannier tank No. L99, a London & North Western Railway first class royal dining car and vintage coaching stock examples from the London Chatham & Dover Railway, Great Northern Railway and Manchester, Sheffield & Lincolnshire Railway. Future plans include a proposed reconnection to the national network which will enable steam trains to operate between Aylesbury and Calvert, via Quainton.

Chinnor & Princes Risborough Railway

Chinnor Station
Nr Princes Risborough
Bucks HP27 9EL

Tel: 01844 353535 (talking timetable)
Route: Chinnor to Wainhill
Length: 31/2 miles
Gauge: Standard

Right GWR 0-6-0PT No. 1638 at work on the Chinnor & Princes Risborough Railway, October 1 1995 (*Mike Esau*)

Left Ex-GWR 0-6-0PT No. L99, in London Transport livery, at the Buckinghamshire Railway Centre (*Phil Marsh*)

Open: Weekends and bank holidays Easter to October
Facilities: Car park, shop, refreshments

The Chinnor & Princes Risborough, one of the newer preservation projects, has re-opened part of the closed GWR Watlington branch from Chinnor to its connection with the main network at Princes Risborough. The line was originally opened in 1872 and taken over by the GWR in 1883. Passenger traffic ceased in 1957 but the section to Chinnor remained open until 1989 to serve the cement works there. Trains run from Chinnor to the junction with the former Thame branch. Visiting steam engines from other lines have recently been an added feature. The line parallels the Icknield Way and passes through attractive countryside with views across the Vale of Whiteleaf. Once the link with the Chiltern line has been made at Princes Risborough the long-term plan is to extend the line back to Aston Rowant. A new ticket office and waiting room, using a Cambrian Railway six-wheel coach dating from 1895, was opened at Chinnor station in December 1995.

Cholsey & Wallingford Railway

PO Box 16
Wallingford
Oxon OX10 0NF

Tel: 01491 835067 (talking timetable)
Route: Cholsey to Wallingford
Length: 2¼ miles
Gauge: Standard
Open: Most Sundays and bank holidays. Telephone for details
Facilities: Car park, shop, refreshments, museum, model railway

Opened in 1892 the ex-GWR branch line to Wallingford was closed by BR in 1965. Since then the preservation society has been attempting to re-open the line, and limited services with a borrowed locomotive ran until 1990, when the line bought its first engine. A Light Railway Order was granted in 1995 and

soon trains will connect with the national network at Cholsey on the main line to Paddington. However, until permission is granted, trains cannot enter Cholsey station and services terminate just short of here.

Colonel Stephens Museum

Tenterden Town Station
Station Road
Tenterden
Kent TN30 6HN

Tel: 01580 765155
Open: Similar to Kent & East Sussex Railway. Telephone for details
Facilities: Car park, refreshments, facilities for disabled

A new museum, opening in 1996 (the centenary year of the 1896 Light Railways Act) which replaces the Colonel Stephens Railway Collection previously exhibited at the Tenterden & District Museum. The new museum will give an account of Colonel Stephens' family background (his father was a member of the pre-Raphaelite Brotherhood of painters); his career as light railway promoter, engineer and manager; and Stephens' career as a Territorial Army officer. Included will also be Stephens' assistant and eventual successor W H Austen. The exhibition will cover the 16 railways with which Stephens was associated, including the nearby Kent & East Sussex, and of those lines proposed but not built. Exhibits will include relics, posters, maps, models and ephemera, a reconstruction of Stephens' office in Tonbridge and various tableaux showing aspects of light railway activity.

Didcot Railway Centre

The Great Western Society
Didcot
Oxon OX11 7NJ

Tel: 01235 817200
Route: Within Railway Centre site
Length: ½ mile

Gauge: Standard and Broad Gauge (7ft 0¼in)
Open: Weekends all year, daily Easter to end September. Telephone for details of steaming days
Facilities: Car park, shop, refreshments, picnic site, small relics display, rides on Steam Days

The Great Western Society, founded in 1961, moved its base to the former BR engine shed at Didcot in 1967 and now evokes all the atmosphere of a working GWR running shed. Now housing the largest collection of GWR locomotives and rolling stock it is also frequently visited by other locomotives employed on steam specials. Locomotives on display include 'Castle' class 4-6-0 No. 5051 *Drysllwyn Castle*, 'Hall' class 4-6-0 No. 5900 *Hinderton Hall* and former Wantage Tramway 0-4-0 well tank *Shannon*, built in 1857. Short rides are given on two demonstration lines within the site, which also boasts a rebuilt small country station complete with working signalbox, originally used at Radstock. A short section of Brunel's broad gauge (7ft 0¼in), with a section of mixed-gauge trackwork, has also been built. On Steam Days demonstrations are given using the restored Travelling Post Office. Work is proceeding on the construction of a library which will house the Society's collection of books and papers relating to the Great Western Railway.

Drusillas Zoo Park Railway

Alfriston
East Sussex BN26 5QS

Tel: 01323 870234
Route: Within Zoo Park
Length: 400yd
Gauge: 2ft
Open: Daily except Christmas
Facilities: Car park, facilities for disabled

A narrow gauge railway that runs through Drusillas Zoo Park, home to a collection of rare

Right GWR 0-4-2T No. 1466 on the 'branch line' at Didcot Railway Centre *(C F D Whetmath)*

breeds of cattle and other farm animals. The Zoo Park was founded by Douglas Ann in 1930 and a 9¼in gauge railway was opened in 1935 but was closed during World War II. Following the end of the war the railway was rebuilt to 2ft gauge and has been operating ever since. Locomotives used are a steam outline Ruston, built in 1943, and two Simplexes built in 1948 and 1965 respectively. Passengers are carried on two sets of five four-wheeled carriages on a journey that gives excellent views of the South Downs and through the llama paddock.

Eastbourne Miniature Steam Railway

Lottbridge Drove
Eastbourne
East Sussex BN23 6NS

Tel: 01323 520229
Route: Circular within site
Length: 1,300yd
Gauge: 7¼in
Open: Daily from end March to end September
Facilities: Car park, shop, refreshments, indoor model railway, LGB garden railway, picnic site, angling, nature walk

This popular miniature railway was opened by the Wadey family in 1992. The single track route is predominantly flat and meanders around a 5½-acre lake through newly-planted woodland, cuttings, tunnel, bridges and over an automatic pedestrian level crossing, passing engine shed, turntable and sidings. Locomotives operated include coal-fired 4-6-0 *Royal Green Jackets* and a Fowler 4F 0-6-0 *Rachel*. Future plans include doubling the single track to enable more trains to operate.

Eastleigh Lakeside Railway

Lakeside
Doncaster Drove
Off Wide Lane
Eastleigh
Hants

Tel: 01703 636612
Route: Around lakes
Length: 1¼ miles
Gauge: 7¼in
Open: Weekends all year and during school holidays
Facilities: Picnic site, shop

This miniature railway crosses Lakeside Park and skirts a large lake all within sight of Eastleigh railway works. It was opened in 1991 and motive power consists of one Swiss-style diesel hydraulic and three steam locomotives. The latter are 4-8-4 *Francis Henry Lloyd*, freelance scale 'Atlantic' 4-4-2 *William Baker* and large narrow gauge 2-4-2 tender locomotive *Sandy River*. A 10¼in gauge 4-6-2 *The Monarch* is also based at the railway. An open weekend for visiting locomotives is also arranged each year. (telephone for details)

East Herts Miniature Railway

Van Hage Garden Centre
Great Amwell
Nr Ware
Herts

Tel: 0181 366 7300 after 6pm
Route: Within garden centre
Length: ¼ mile
Gauge: 7¼in
Open: Weekends all year, Thursdays in school holidays
Facilities: Car park, garden centre facilities

This miniature railway, situated in a garden centre, opened in 1977, has carried over 500,000 passengers and raised £12,000 for local children's charities. The route is a double oval of track with a diamond crossing and is situated in a field in the outer garden centre area. Motive power consists of a steam 0-4-2 *Tinkerbell* and two petrol hydrostatic locomotives with passengers being carried on seven sit-astride and two sit-in coaches.

East Kent Light Railway

Shepherdswell Station
Shepherdswell
Nr Dover
Kent

Tel: 01304 832042
Route: Shepherdswell to Eythorne
Length: 2 miles
Gauge: Standard
Open: Weekends Easter to December and bank holidays
Facilities: Car park, refreshments, picnic site, museum, miniature railway

The East Kent Light Railway was constructed between 1911 and 1924 to serve the Kent coalfield and originally ran from Shepherdswell, on the main Dover to Canterbury line, to the port of Richborough. The latter was not reached until 1928 by which time the port was already in decline. The line was built by Colonel H F Stephens, the famous railway engineer and supporter of light railways (see Colonel Stephens Museum p.48) and passengers were first carried in 1916. However the line depended mainly on the coal industry and the decline of this had a severe impact on the railway's revenue. Passenger services ceased in 1948 and by 1953 the whole railway beyond Tilmanstone had been closed, The remaining three-mile section was kept open for colliery traffic until 1984 and the line was finally closed in 1987. A preservation group was formed in 1985 and work started on restoring Shepherdswell station and clearing the overgrown line in 1989. By 1993 a Light Railway Order was granted and BR agreed to sell the trackbed to the Society. Regular train services now run over the two miles through Golgotha Tunnel to Eythorne and future plans include extending the line to Tilmanstone Colliery. Motive power includes a diesel multiple unit, various diesels and a former 0-6-0 colliery engine currently being restored.

Elham Valley Line Trust

Peene Yard
Peene
Newington
Folkestone
Kent CT18 8BA

Tel: 01303 273690
Open: Weekends April to September
Facilities: Car park, refreshments, picnic site

A railway museum, devoted to the former South Eastern & Chatham Railway line from Canterbury to Folkestone, built in 1884 and closed in 1947, situated in a recreated 1934 station building. This contains SECR artefacts and ephemera and a 50ft-long 'N' gauge model railway depicting the 16^1/$_2$ miles from Folkestone to Canterbury through the Elham Valley in the 1930's. Also included on display are a replica of an SECR Class E1 0-6-0 tank locomotive and a fully working signalbox. Future plans include the possibility of opening a 10^1/$_4$in gauge miniature railway from the museum to the village of Newington. The Eurotunnel Exhibition Centre is only ^{1}/$_4$-mile from the museum.

Great Bush Railway

Tinkers Park Collection
Hadlow Down
Uckfield
Sussex

Route: Within site of annual steam rally
Gauge: 2ft
Open: Once a year on the date of annual traction engine rally. See press for details

The passenger-carrying Great Bush Railway is part of a large annual event that includes steam engines, military vehicles and stationary engines. The 2ft gauge line operates for only two days a year, when regular passenger trains are hauled by one of five resident diesel locomotives. The railway also has five battery electric and two steam 0-4-0T engines.

A powerful combination on the 7^1/$_4$in gauge Great Cockrow Railway (*Great Cockrow Railway*)

Great Cockrow Railway

Hardwick Lane
Lyne
Nr Chertsey
Surrey

Tel: 01932 225500 (Monday to Friday)
Route: Hardwick Central to Cockrow Hill and loops
Length: 2 miles
Gauge: 7^1/$_4$in
Open: Sunday afternoons May to October
Facilities: Car park, refreshments, facilities for disabled

Originally named the Greywood Central Railway this unique miniature passenger-carrying line was established by Sir John Samuel, of Burwood Park, Walton-on-Thames, in 1946. On his death in 1962 the entire line was purchased by the publisher Ian Allan who transferred it to Lyne. It was re-opened on its new site in 1968 and since then has been much expanded to its present layout, which includes three distinctive train rides and a 45ft-long viaduct. A total of 20 steam locomotives are on the roster and at least seven of these should be on duty on any operating day. Turntables at each terminus enable all the engines to be turned after each journey and passengers are carried on four-seater vehicles, of which there are 23. The railway is fully signalled, using both semaphore and colour-light signals, with three signalboxes and four stations. The booking office at Hardwick Central was originally situated at Ravenscourt Park on the District Line.

Great Whipsnade Railway

Whipsnade Wild Animal Park
Dunstable
Beds LU6 2LF

Tel: 01582 872171 ext.2270
Route: Circuit within wild animal paddocks
Length: 2 miles

Gauge: 2ft 6in
Open: During zoo opening times. Telephone for details
Facilities: Car park, shop, refreshments, facilities for disabled

Built in 1970 by Pleasurerail this line was originally named the Whipsnade & Umfolozi Light Railway and carried visitors through the white rhino herd at Whipsnade Zoo. In 1985, when the rhinos were relocated, the name changed to the Great Whipsnade Railway, and in 1990 Pleasurerail was taken over by the zoo operators. The station is situated near the dolphinarium and the line now runs through paddocks containing the animals of Asia. The majority of the railway equipment, including steam locomotives built earlier this century, came from the former Bowaters Papermill Railway in Kent (see Sittingbourne & Kemsley Light Railway p.62) and passengers are carried on coaches built from former pulp wagon bogie frames. Future plans include a Wine & Dine train, driving courses and extension of the track further round the Park.

Hollycombe Steam Collection

Iron Hill
Liphook
Hants GU30 7LP

Tel: 01428 724900
Route: Within grounds of Hollycombe House
Length: 1½ miles
Gauge: 2ft and standard
Open: Sunday afternoons and bank holidays Easter to October
Facilities: Car park, shop, refreshments, steam-operated fairground and 7¼in gauge miniature railway

The 2ft gauge steam operated Quarry Railway climbs through woodland within the grounds of Hollycombe House before giving passengers wonderful views of the South Downs from its summit. The shorter standard gauge Hollycombe Tramway features Hawthorn Leslie 0-4-0ST

Commander B. A large collection of traction engines and fairground rides is also operated for the public.

Hythe Pier Railway

The Ferry Office
Prospect Place
Hythe
Hampshire SO45 6AU

Tel: 01703 840722
Route: Along the length of Hythe Pier
Length: ½ mile
Gauge: 2ft
Open: Daily except Christmas Day and Boxing Day

This little electric railway carries passengers along the length of Hythe Pier to connect with ferries to Southampton Town Quay. Hythe Pier was opened in 1880 and in 1909 a tramway, using a hand-propelled trolley, was built to convey luggage to and from the ferry. In 1922 the line was electrified on the third-rail principle and now the small three-coach trains, powered by a diminutive electric locomotive, still ply to and fro along the pier with their load of ferry passengers. Operating the service are two Brush four-wheel, three-speed 100 volt DC, motor units and four timber-framed 18-seat coaches.

Isle of Wight Steam Railway

The Railway Station
Haven Street
Isle of Wight PO33 4DS

Tel: 01983 882204/01983 884343
Route: Smallbrook Junction to Wootton
Length: 5 miles
Gauge: Standard
Open: March to October and Santa Specials in December. Telephone for details
Facilities: Car park, shop, refreshments, museum, picnic site, facilities for disabled (all at Haven Street)

Originally opened in 1875 as the Ryde & Newport Railway and eventually becoming part of the network of rural branch lines run by the Southern Railway on the Isle of Wight. Because of their isolation from the mainland the railways on the island used a collection of second-hand locomotives and rolling stock. The island rail system, except for the section from Ryde Pier Head to Shanklin, was closed by BR in 1966 and a preservation group moved in to Haven Street in 1971. Services to Wootton restarted in 1977 and to Ashey and the new station at Smallbrook Junction in 1991, where connection can be made with the electrified Island Line, which operates former London Underground tube stock between Ryde and Shanklin. The ancient and beautifully preserved locomotives and rolling stock, some dating back to the 19th century, all contribute to the Victorian atmosphere that pervades the railway. Included in the line-up are former London Brighton & South Coast Railway Class A1X 0-6-0 tanks, No. W8 *Freshwater* and No. 32640, built in 1876 and 1878 respectively, and London & South Western Railway Class O2 0-4-4 tank No. W24 *Calbourne*. The Isle of Wight Steam Railway is currently liaising with Island Line to investigate possible steam operation to Ryde and is also looking into a future extension of the line westwards to Newport. The railway won the Ian Allan Independent Railway of the Year award in 1995.

Kent & East Sussex Railway

Tenterden Town Station
Tenterden
Kent TN30 6HE

Tel: 01580 765155/01580 762943 (talking timetable)/01580 766428 (special events)
Route: Tenterden to Northiam
Length: 7 miles
Gauge: Standard
Open: March to December. Telephone for details

Right LSWR Class '02' 0-4-4T No. 24 *Calbourne* at Smallbrook Junction on the Isle of Wight Steam Railway, September 3 1991 *(Mike Esau)*

Facilities: Car park, shop, refreshments, museum (see p.48), picnic site, Wine & Dine train, facilities for disabled

Originally known as the Rother Valley Railway, the first light railway in the world was built and owned by the legendary Colonel Holman Stephens. Opened in sections from Robertsbridge to Rolvenden in 1900, to the Cinque Port of Tenterden in 1903, and eventually reaching Headcorn in 1905, the line changed its name to the Kent & East Sussex Railway in 1904. It is one of England's classic railways, epitomised by sharp curves, steep gradients and remote country stations. As was usual with all of Colonel Stephens' 16 railways, the Kent & East Sussex always led a very precarious existence but managed to survive through to BR ownership in 1948 before being closed in 1961. A preservation group, eventually based at Tenterden, was quickly formed but it was not until 1974 that services started running. Wittersham Road station was opened in 1978 and the present terminus at Northiam in 1990. An extension is planned to Bodiam and Robertsbridge where the line will connect with the national system. Trains are mainly steam-hauled and the railway owns a collection of superbly restored four and six-wheeled Victorian coaches. Locomotives include the diminutive former SECR 'P' Class 0-6-0 tank No. 1556, built in 1909, powerful ex-War Department types and a Norwegian 2-6-0 tender engine.

Kew Bridge Steam Museum

Green Dragon Lane
Brentford
Middx TW8 0EN

Tel: 0181 568 4757
Route: Within museum site
Length: 700ft
Gauge: 2ft
Open: Museum open daily except Christmas. Railway operates 2nd and last weekend of month from March to November
Facilities: Car park, shop, refreshments

A 2ft gauge railway operates at this museum, originally a 19th century pumping station for London's water supply network, which is the home to five working Cornish steam beam engines. *Grand Junction 90* is the world's largest working beam engine. Trains are operated by restored 0-4-0 steam locomotive *Wendy* built by Bagnall in 1919 and a diesel. Passengers are carried in former National Coal Board manrider wagons.

Knebworth Miniature Railway

Knebworth Park
Knebworth
Nr Stevenage
Herts SG3 6PY

Tel: 01438 812661
Route: Within grounds of Knebworth House
Length: 1,200yd
Gauge: 10^1/$_4$in
Open: Easter to end September. Telephone for details
Facilities: Car park, shop, refreshments, stately home

Three diesels and one petrol locomotive are employed on this miniature passenger-carrying railway that runs in the grounds of Knebworth House. The present line was opened in 1991 and replaced a previous 2ft gauge system.

Lavender Line

Isfield Station
Isfield
Nr Uckfield
East Sussex TN22 5XB

Tel: 01825 750515
Route: Within station site
Length: 1 mile
Gauge: Standard
Open: Sundays March to December, daily during August
Facilities: Car park, shop, refreshments, museum, picnic site, facilities for disabled

Situated only a few miles from the Bluebell Railway (see p.44) the Lavender Line is based at the beautifully restored station of Isfield. Originally part of the London Brighton & South Coast Railway's route from Eridge to Lewes, Isfield station was closed by BR in 1969. It was bought by David Milham in 1983 and, along with the signalbox, was restored to its former Victorian glory. In 1992 it was sold to a preservation group, who operate both steam and diesel trains along a short distance of track within the station site.

Leighton Buzzard Railway

Page's Park Station
Billington Road
Leighton Buzzard LU7 8TN

Tel: 01525 373888 (talking timetable)
Route: Page's Park to Stonehenge Works
Length: 2^3/$_4$ miles
Gauge: 2ft
Open: Late March to mid October and then December. Telephone for details
Facilities: Car park, shop, refreshments, museum, picnic site, combined rail/canal cruise, facilities for disabled

Built during the World War 1 to transport sand from pits near Leighton Buzzard this former industrial narrow gauge line was saved from closure by a preservation group who started to operate trains in 1968. Now home to 11 steam and 40 diesel locomotives, originating from West Africa, India, Spain and Britain, trains operate from the railway's headquarters at Page's Park running behind housing estates and into open country before arriving at Stonehenge Works, a former brickworks. It is here that many items of the railway's historic collection are housed. Sharp curves and steep gradients abound on this fascinating line. The oldest working locomotive on the railway is the 1877-built 0-4-0 vertical-boilered *Chaloner*, and visiting locomotives are a common sight on special events days.

Right 0-4-0ST *Woto* and 0-4-0VBT *Chaloner* meet on the Leighton Buzzard Railway, September 11 1994 *(Mike Esau)*

London Toy & Model Museum

21/23 Craven Hill
London W2 3EN

Tel: 0171 706 8000/0171 402 5222 (recorded
information)
Open: Daily except Christmas Day, Boxing Day
and New Year's Day
Facilities: Refreshments, shop, function rooms

A large and unique collection of toys and models,
including trains, is displayed in 20 themed
galleries at this museum. Railway enthusiasts can
amuse themselves in the 'HO' Gauge Gallery, the
Steam Room Gallery and the Railway Gallery.
Electric trains operate on a garden railway and
steam-operated gauge '1' to gauge $7^{1}/_{4}$in lines are
in action on Sundays.

London Transport Museum

Covent Garden
London WC2E 7BB

Tel: 0171 379 6344/0171 886 8557
Open: Daily except Christmas
Facilities: Shop, refreshments, library, facilities
for disabled

A large collection of public transport road and rail
vehicles used in London from Victorian times to
the present day is housed in the former Flower
Market which dates back to 1870. The museum
was extended during 1993 with increased display
space and spectacular new mezzanine floors.
Included on display are a 1866-built Metropolitan
Railway 4-4-0 condensing tank No. 23 and a
1922-built 1,200 horsepower Bo-Bo electric
locomotive *John Hampden*, Wotton Tramway
traction engine locomotive No. 807 built in 1872,
as well as examples of early underground electric
trains such as the 1890-built City & South
London Railway 'Padded Cell' car. Visitors to the
museum can 'drive' an Underground train on a
simulator and also take part in signals and points
demonstrations. Models, artefacts, posters and an
audio-visual display are included. The museum

has a large photographic archive section containing over 100,000 black and white photographs of London Transport and its predecessors.

Mid-Hants Railway

Alresford Station
Alresford
Hants SO24 9JG

Tel: 01962 733810/01962 734866 (talking timetable)
Route: Alresford to Alton (BR connection)
Length: 10 miles
Gauge: Standard
Open: March to October and Santa Specials in December. Telephone for details
Facilities: Car parks, refreshments, shops, picnic site, Wine & Dine trains, Real Ale trains, footplate experiences, facilities for disabled

Opened in 1865 the railway between Alton and Winchester, known as the Mid-Hants (Alton) Railway, was an important link for the armed services between Aldershot and Portsmouth. Heavily used in both World Wars it was also an important diversionary route for main line trains between Woking and Winchester. An important local traffic included the transport of locally-grown watercress, which is now used by the present company as its marketing title. Up to 1923 the railway formed part of the London & South Western Railway network before being swallowed up in the newly formed Southern Railway. Finally closed by BR in 1973 the current section of the line was soon taken over by a preservation group who started services, initially from Alresford to Ropley, in 1977. Services to Alton, where there is an important link with the national network, started in 1985. Steam-hauled trains operate over this steeply-graded line, locally known as 'The Alps', necessitating the use of large and impressive locomotives,

Left LSWR Class 'M7' 0-4-4T No. 30053 on a charter freight at Medstead & Four Marks station on the Mid-Hants Railway, March 13 1995 *(Mike Esau)*

including ex-SR Bulleid 'West Country' class 'Pacifics' No. 34016 *Bodmin* and No. 34105 *Swanage*. Visiting locomotives can also be regularly seen hard at work on special event days through the year. The stations along the line are all beautifully restored to different periods in the history of the railway, and of special note is the carefully pruned 60-year old topiary at Ropley station, where the Mid-Hants also has its extensive workshops and engine shed.

Mizens Railway

Mizens Farm
Chertsey Road
Woking
Surrey

Tel: 01483 720801
Route: Triple circuit within farm
Length: 1/2 mile
Gauge: 71/4in
Open: Easter Sunday to October, first and third Sunday afternoons of each month
Facilities: Car park

Operated by the Woking Miniature Railway Society, founded in 1989, this railway creates a 1950s atmosphere in which passenger-carrying trains operate in a pleasant four-acre rural location. Both standard and narrow gauge miniature steam locomotives, plus some diesels, haul passengers on this fully-signalled route close to the banks of the River Bourne.

Norton Ash Railway

Norton Ash Nursery
Teynham
Nr Faversham
Kent

Tel: 01795 521549
Route: Within nursery grounds
Length: 200yd
Gauge: 9in
Open: Telephone for details

A miniature passenger-carrying line that runs through nursery grounds and operates 4-4-0 steam locomotive *Robin*, rebuilt from an 0-4-4 tank.

Old Kiln Agricultural Museum

Reeds Road
Tilford
Farnham
Surrey

Tel: 01252 792300/01252 795571
Open: Telephone for details

Housing a collection of farm and household equipment this museum also has a 1/4-mile long 2ft gauge steam operated railway that runs on certain days.

Pendon Museum

Long Wittenham
Nr Abingdon
Oxfordshire OX14 4QD

Tel: 01865 407365
Open: Weekend afternoons early January to early December and bank holiday weekends Easter to August
Facilities: Shop, refreshments

The museum was started in 1954 by Roye England to capture in miniature the beauty of the Vale of White Horse landscape and villages as they existed in the 1930s and to reveal the excitement of the Great Western Railway as it was during the heyday of steam. Since the beginning, the museum has been a centre for modelling excellence. There are three major exhibits at the museum:
 - A 70ft-long model of village life in the Vale of White Horse
 - An imaginary GWR branch line in Dartmoor with extensive train operations
 - The formative Madder Valley model railway, built by John Ahern
Although work has been progressing for over 40

Above 2-6-0 *The Lady Jennifer* on the 10¼in gauge Polytechnic Stadium Railway *(N R Knight)*

years, the Vale scene is still 'under construction' and another ten years of work is not hard to imagine. However, the Vale is already breathtaking to view, and visitors who return are always delighted to note the progress. Not only can you see one of the finest modelling panoramas in England, you can see it being created.

Polytechnic Stadium Railway

Polytechnic Sports Ground
Hartington Road
Chiswick
London W4

Length: ¹/₂ mile
Gauge: 10¹/₄in
Open: Friday evenings in the summer

A miniature railway runs around the sports field perimeter from an outer terminal station named 'Willow End'. Steam locomotives operating on

the line include BR Class 4MT 4-6-0 No. 75080 and LMS Stanier 2-6-0 No. 2950. An LMS 4-6-2 is under construction.

Queen Mary's Railway

Former Queen Mary's Hospital site
Carshalton
Surrey

Route: Within grounds of hospital
Length: ¹/₂ mile
Gauge: 10¹/₄in
Open: Sunday afternoons May to September. See note below
Facilities: Car park, facilities for disabled

This miniature railway was built in 1967 by a local model engineer and has been extended twice. From the main station, situated next to the cricket pitch in the old hospital grounds, the line climbs a gradient of 1-in-40 before rounding a copse on the level and climbing again at 1-in-50

to the terminus at the children's zoo. One Simplex-designed steam locomotive, *Titan*, two Hymek diesel hydraulics and a battery-operated tram engine operate trains which also include two coaches adapted for wheelchairs.

Note Due to the hospital's closure the railway may need to close in late 1996 and will be relocated in 1997.

Romney, Hythe & Dymchurch Railway

New Romney Station
New Romney
Kent TN28 8PL

Tel: 01797 362353
Route: Hythe to Dungeness
Length: 13¹/₂ miles
Gauge: 15in
Open: Daily Easter to end September, weekends March and October
Facilities: Car park, shop, refreshments, toy and model museum, picnic site, facilities for disabled

The world's smallest public railway, from Hythe to Dungeness, was conceived and built by the wealthy racing driver Captain Jack Howey. No money was spared to produce an accurate one-third scale working miniature of a main line railway. As in full-size practice the line was double track and signalled, engines were replicas of LNER and Canadian express locomotives, and passengers were carried in bogie carriages. The first section of the line, from Hythe to New Romney, was opened in 1927 and the then Duke of York, later to become King George VI, had the honour of driving the first train. The line was extended westward to Dungeness lighthouse, where the line forms a complete loop, in 1929. In the pre-War years the line was very popular with holidaymakers and during World War II an armoured train was built complete with machine

Right Bo-Bo diesel No. 12 *John Southland* enters Hythe station on the 15in gauge Romney Hythe & Dymchurch Railway *(AA Photo Library)*

guns. The RHDR also played an important part in transporting materials for Operation Pluto (Pipe Line Under the Ocean) preceding the D-Day landings. The period after the war brought mixed fortunes for the little railway and, with falling passenger receipts, losses mounted after Howey's death until the line was first put up for sale in 1968. After rumours that the RHDR was going to be moved lock, stock and barrel to the West Country, a consortium headed by W H McAlpine bought the line in 1971 and proceeded to restore it to its former glory. It currently boasts 11 steam locomotives, two diesels (used on the regular school train during term time), and over 65 assorted coaches including the unique buffet observation car. To add to the authentic main line atmosphere the railway boasts a large engine shed, turntable and workshop at New Romney, and an overall roof covers the three platforms at Hythe terminus. During peak periods trains run every 45 minutes, at speeds up to 25mph, and the timetable features a non-stop express along the whole length of the line on summer Saturdays.

Romsey Signal Box Project

Winchester Road
Romsey
Hants

Tel: 01794 522979
Open: First Sunday of each month plus special events
Facilities: Car park in nearby Romsey Infants School

A fully restored and working signalbox on its own land next to the Romsey to Southampton railway line. The box closed in 1982 and was re-opened in 1992, and is now completely fitted out with operating signalling equipment. A visitor centre, formed of ex-Southern Railway meat container vans, contains additional items of interest and there is also a visitor trail and development of the canalside location.

Royal Victoria Railway

Royal Victoria Country Park
Netley
Southampton
Hampshire SO31 5GA

Tel: 01344 21286
Route: Within grounds of 200-acre country park
Length: 1 mile
Gauge: 10¼in
Open: Opening daily Spring 1996. Telephone for details
Facilities: Refreshments, picnic sites, children's playground

The Royal Victoria Railway runs close to the LSWR Netley station - Royal Victoria Hospital branch line opened in 1900 and closed in 1955. A few remaining standard gauge railway lines are still visible today. The original miniature railway on this site opened in 1989 and was removed in 1995. Track was relaid and very much extended in Autumn 1995. Locomotives operating on the line are a narrow gauge 2-6-0 steam tank and a Bo-Bo narrow gauge diesel hydraulic. The journey starts at Chapell Road station and involves gradients of 1-in-80 and a tunnel before reaching Tea Room Halt. It then passes the engine shed and through dense undergrowth before levelling out, providing passengers with good views of Southampton Water, finally returning to the main station. Future plans include improvements to the stations, a signalbox with signalling and acquiring more locomotives.

Ruislip Lido Railway

Reservoir Road
Ruislip
Middx

Tel: 0181 863 2069/01895 622595 (talking timetable)
Route: Within grounds of Ruislip Lido
Length: 1½ miles
Gauge: 12in
Open: Sundays throughout year, daily Easter to October except Mondays and Fridays in April, May, September and October
Facilities: Car park, picnic site, facilities for disabled

Three diesel locomotives and a half-size Festiniog Railway steam locomotive operate on this miniature passenger-carrying railway within the grounds of Ruislip Lido country park. The line is run by a dedicated team of volunteers and plans are in hand to extend the line for a mile towards the main car park entrance.

Science Museum

Exhibition Road
South Kensington
London SW7 2DD

Tel: 0171 938 8000/0171 938 9788 (disabled persons' helpline)
Open: Daily except December 24-26
Facilities: Refreshments, shop, facilities for disabled

Opened as the South Kensington Museum in 1857 on land purchased with the profits from the 1851 Great Exhibition. The present transport gallery, opened in 1967, includes a static display of historic locomotives which forms a small part of this famous museum. Exhibits include the Wylam Colliery *Puffing Billy* (1813), *Rocket* and *Sans Pareil* locomotives (both dating from 1829) from the Liverpool & Manchester Railway and GWR 'Castle' class 4-6-0 *Caerphilly Castle* (1923). Many high-quality models of locomotives and rolling stock are also displayed. Future plans include a new extension building to the west of the existing buildings, which is currently being planned and designed. The railway collection is administered as part of the National Railway Collection, based at the National Railway Museum, York (see p.130).

Right GWR 'Castle' class 4-6-0 No. 4073 *Caerphilly Castle* being loaded on to a road transporter at Park Royal for its final journey to the Science Museum, June 3 1961 *(R C Riley)*

Sittingbourne & Kemsley Railway

Off Milton Lane
Sittingbourne
Kent

Tel: 01634 852672/01795 424899 (talking timetable)
Route: Sittingbourne (Milton Creek) to Kemsley Down
Length: 2 miles
Gauge: 2ft 6in
Open: Sundays Easter to October, Tuesdays, Wednesdays and Saturdays in August
Facilities: Car park, refreshments, shop, picnic site, museum

This industrial railway was originally built in 1906 by Edward Lloyd Ltd to carry paper from a wharf on Milton Creek to a mill at Sittingbourne and later extended to carry logs and woodpulp from a wharf on the River Swale at Ridham to the papermill. In 1924 a further papermill, served by the railway, was opened at Kemsley and more locomotives were purchased to cope with the extra traffic. Two of the three original locomotives, Kerr Stuart 0-4-2STs *Premier* and *Leader*, can still be seen at work on the line today. In 1948 the Bowater Group purchased the company and its railway, with further locomotive acquisitions, and continued to run it until 1965 when road transport was introduced. The Locomotive Club of Great Britain took over, on loan from Bowaters, the two miles of track between Sittingbourne and Kemsley in 1969 and by Easter 1970 the line was open for passengers. Trains are now mainly steam-hauled using industrial locomotives and coaches, many from the original railway, including four coaches from the former Chattenden & Upnor Military Railway on the Isle of Grain. A concrete viaduct at Sittingbourne, one of the first reinforced concrete structures built, is currently under repair and when this work is completed the railway will re-open the presently closed section.

Left Kerr Stuart 0-4-2ST *Melior* on the Sittingbourne & Kemsley Railway in 1994 *(G Siviour)*

Southall Railway Centre

Southall
Middx UB2 4PL

Tel: 0181 574 1529 (evenings and weekends only)
Open: Static display on most weekends and bank holidays, telephone for details of steaming days
Facilities: Shop, refreshments

Based in the old GWR engine shed at Southall, closed by BR in 1986, is a collection of eleven steam and diesel locomotives and items of rolling stock. Operated by the GWR Preservation Group the Centre opened to the public in 1994 and has various operational days through the year, when locomotives are steamed. Former LNER 4-6-2 *Flying Scotsman* was recently being overhauled at the centre.

Spa Valley Railway

Eridge Station
Tunbridge Wells
Kent TN3 9LE

Tel: 01892 862140
Route: Tunbridge Wells West to Eridge
Length: 5¹/₂ miles
Gauge: Standard
Open: Telephone for details

A recent scheme to re-open the former London Brighton & South Coast route from Tunbridge Wells to Eridge which was closed by BR in 1985. The scenic route is through attractive countryside; it is hoped that the Tunbridge Wells to Groombridge section will be re-opened late in 1996 and Eridge by early 1997. Motive power at the moment consists of Peckett 0-6-0 saddle tank *Fonmon* with ex-BR Mark 1 coaches. A railway museum is situated in the four-road locomotive shed at Tunbridge Wells. Locomotives and rolling stock from the former North Downs Steam Railway have recently been moved to the Tunbridge Wells site.

Swanley New Barn Railway

New Barn Park
New Barn Lane
Swanley
Kent

Route: Within Swanley New Barn Park
Length: 900yd
Gauge: 7¹/₄in
Open: Weekends, bank holidays and school holidays from Good Friday to end October, weather permitting
Facilities: Car park, refreshments, picnic site, boating lake, playground

This miniature railway was originally run by the local council but was taken over in 1987 by a local society. The railway celebrates ten years of service in 1996. Trains depart from Lakeside station in New Barn Park, passing the signalbox, containing a 35-lever frame from Gloucester Road, and climb to the summit of the line before reaching New Barn Halt, adjacent to the car park. From here the line runs downhill and back into Lakeside, with its three-platform terminus. A large number of locomotives are available to run the service, including one battery-powered, four diesels and five steam. Rolling stock consists of 17 sit-astride coaches plus various other vehicles.

Syon Park Miniature Railway

Syon Park
Brentford
Middx TW8 8JF

Tel: 0181 560 0881
Route: Within Syon Park gardens
Length: 440yd
Gauge: 10¹/₄in
Open: Weekends and bank holidays April to October
Facilities: Car park, refreshments

The miniature railway at famous Syon Park was built in 1993, extended in 1994, and links the Great Conservatory with the picnic area at 'Flora's Lawn'. The route passes through parkland and woodland famous as a fascinating example of Capability Brown's landscape artistry. Two steam locomotives operate services – a streamlined LMS 'Coronation' class 4-6-2 and a 'Royal Scot' class 4-6-0. Future plans include eventual extensions of the railway around a major part of the gardens.

Thames Ditton Miniature Railway

Claygate Lane
Thames Ditton
Surrey KT7 0DL

Tel: 0181 398 3985
Route: Circular within club grounds
Length: 1,100yd
Gauge: 3¹/₂in, 5in and 7¹/₄in
Open: Afternoons on first Sunday of each month and Bank Holiday Sundays and Mondays from Easter to early October
Facilities: Car park, shop, refreshments, picnic site

Operated by the Malden & District Society of Model Engineers this club railway features a 550yd ground level 7¹/₄in gauge miniature railway and 550yd of raised mixed gauge (3¹/₂in and 5in) line all within view of the Waterloo to Woking main line. The railway was founded in 1936 at New Malden and relocated to its present site in 1948. Most of the steam locomotives operating on the line are privately owned and a good variety can normally be seen giving passenger rides on operating days.

Vanstone Woodland Railway

Vanstone Park Garden Centre
Hitchin Road
Codicote
Herts

Tel: 01438 820412
Route: Within Vanstone Park Garden Centre
Length: 600yd
Gauge: 10¹/₄in

Open: Weekends and bank holidays
Facilities: Car park, refreshments

This miniature railway operates within a garden centre and was opened in 1986 with relocation of the station in 1995. Trains are operated by two diesel-mechanical locomotives and there are three articulated carriages. The route is in the shape of a dumb-bell with a branch to the station.

Volks Electric Railway

285 Madeira Drive
Brighton BN2 1EN

Tel: 01273 681061
Route: Palace Pier to Brighton Marina Station
Length: 1¼ miles
Gauge: 2ft 8½in
Open: Early April to mid September
Facilities: Car park, refreshments, facilities for disabled

Opened in 1883 by Magnus Volk, the Volks Electric Railway, which was taken over by Brighton Corporation in 1940, was the first electric railway in Britain and runs along the seafront at Brighton. Power is supplied by a third rail and present rolling stock includes cars built in 1892 and 1901 and two open toast-rack cars, built in 1898, from Southend Pier. The railway is a single line operation with three passing loops and three stations, and a total of 13 pedestrian crossings are marked with red lights. Magnus Volk also designed the famous 'Daddy Long Legs', a mixture of tramcar, yacht and seaside pier, which was sadly destroyed in a storm only a few days after its inauguration in 1896. Future plans include new stations to be built at Marina and Pier.

Watford Miniature Railway

Cassiobury Park
Watford
Herts

Route: Within Cassiobury Park

Length: 1,050yd
Gauge: 10¼in
Open: Weekends, school holidays and afternoons May to July and September

Established in 1959, extended in 1963 and again in 1988 this miniature railway operates four steam locomotives and some diesels. Passengers are carried on open articulated sets along an out and return route from the terminus, situated near the children's paddling pool and playground in Cassiobury Park.

Wellington Country Park Miniature Railway

Wellington Country Park
Heckfield
Nr Basingstoke
Hants

Tel: 01734 326067
Route: Within Wellington Country Park
Length: ⅓ mile
Gauge: 7¼in
Open: Daily Easter to early November
Facilities: Car park, refreshments, leisure facilities within park

This miniature railway was opened in 1980 and takes passengers from a four-platform station on a scenic route through the country park, crossing a small lake on a girder bridge and passing through a tunnel. Motive power consists of two narrow gauge outline steam locomotives, due to be replaced in the near future, and a petrol hydraulic engine. Future plans include an extension to the line. The owners also build and maintain locomotives for other miniature railway operators.

Willen Miniature Railway

Willen Lakeside Park
Milton Keynes
Buckinghamshire

Route: Within Willen Lakeside Park

Length: ¼ mile
Gauge: 7¼in
Open: Weekends all year

This short miniature line starts at Willen Halt and runs through the trees past a locomotive shed. Two steam locomotives operate the trains.

Yafford Mill & Farm Museum

Shorwell
Newport
Isle of Wight

Tel: 01983 740610
Route: Within museum site
Length: 450yd
Gauge: 2ft 6in
Open: Daily
Facilities: Car park, refreshments, working water-mill, agricultural museum, animals

This narrow gauge railway, operating within the farm museum site, opened to the public in Easter 1995 and carried 9,000 passengers in its first year of operation. The line runs from a small station and yard through open fields containing a collection of animals, before returning to its starting point. It is hoped to extend the line by another 600yd in 1996. Trains made up of air-braked coaches are hauled by two Hunslet 0-4-0 diesel mechanical locomotives built in 1940 and previously used at the National Tractor Museum.

Wales

1. Bala Lake Railway
2. Brecon Mountain Railway
3. Caerphilly Railway Centre
4. Conwy Valley Railway Museum
5. Corris Railway Museum
6. Fairbourne & Barmouth Steam Railway
7. Festiniog Railway Company
8. Gloddfa Ganol Narrow Gauge Railway Centre
9. Glyn Valley Tramway Group
10. Great Orme Tramway
11. Gwili Steam Railway
12. Joys of Life Visitor Centre
13. Llanberis Lake Railway
14. Llangollen Railway
15. Llechwedd Slate Caverns
16. Llwyfan Cerrig Miniature Railway
17. Narrow Gauge Railway Museum
18. Narrower Gauge Railway
19. The Old Station
20. Penrhyn Castle Industrial Railway Museum
21. Pontypool & Blaenavon Railway
22. Rhiw Valley Railway
23. Rhyl Miniature Railway
24. Snowdon Mountain Railway
25. Swansea Maritime & Industrial Museum
26. Swansea Vale Railway
27. Talyllyn Railway
28. Teifi Valley Railway
29. Vale of Rheidol Light Railway
30. Welsh Highland Railway
31. Welshpool & Llanfair Light Railway
32. Welsh Industrial & Maritime Museum
33. Welsh Slate Museum

Holyhead

CLWYD

Wrexham •

GWYNEDD

Porthmadog, 7,30

Dolgellau

Welshpool

POWYS

Aberystwyth

DYFED

Fishguard

Brecon

Carmarthen

WEST GLAMORGAN

MID GLAMORGAN

GWENT

Merthyr Tydfil

Newport

Swansea

Cardiff

SOUTH GLAMORGAN

65

Bala Lake Railway

The Station
Llanuwchllyn
Bala
Gwynedd LL23 7DD

Tel: 01678 540666
Route: Llanuwchllyn to Bala
Length: 4¹/₂ miles
Gauge: 1ft 11¹/₂in
Open: Early April to end September except certain Mondays in April, May, June and September
Facilities: Car parks, refreshments, picnic site, shop, museum, facilities for disabled

The Bala & Dolgelly Railway opened in 1868 eventually becoming part of the GWR route from Ruabon to Barmouth. The line was eventually closed by BR in 1965 and a scheme for a narrow gauge line along part of the trackbed was proposed in 1971. The present line which skirts the eastern shore of Lake Bala, the largest natural lake in Wales, was re-opened in stages between 1972 and 1976. Passenger trains were initially diesel-hauled but steam services commenced in 1975. Trains are normally operated by two Hunslet 0-4-0 saddle tanks, *Holy War* (built in 1902) and *Maid Marion* (built in 1903) – both originally from the Dinorwic Slate Quarry, with the latter having also worked on the Bressingham and Llanberis Lake railways – and industrial narrow gauge diesels. Passengers are carried in purpose-built carriages. Llanuwchllyn Station, the headquarters of the railway, is a finely preserved example of an original Bala & Dolgelly Railway building. It is planned to extend the line half a mile to a new terminus nearer the town of Bala.

Below Hunslet 0-4-0ST No. 5 *Maid Marian* on the Bala Lake Railway *(AA Photo Library)*

Brecon Mountain Railway

Pant Station
Dowlais
Merthyr Tydfil
Mid-Glamorgan CF48 2UP

Tel: 01685 722988
Route: Pant to Dolygaer
Length: 3¹/₂ miles
Gauge: 1ft 11³/₄in
Open: April to October. Telephone for details
Facilities: Car park, shop, refreshments, picnic site, facilities for disabled

The Brecon & Merthyr Tydfil Junction Railway, opened throughout in 1868, was one of Britain's most spectacularly scenic railways involving tortuous gradients and the single track Torpantau Tunnel. After passing into GWR ownership the line was eventually closed by BR in 1964. In 1972 a scheme to build a narrow gauge railway along part of the disused trackbed was put forward. Construction of the line from Pant to Pontsticill, in the Brecon Beacons National Park, began in 1978 and the opening train ran in 1980. A further 1³/₄ miles along the side of Taf Fechan Reservoir to the present terminus at Dolygaer was opened in 1995 and a further extension of two miles through the 666yd-long Torpantau Tunnel (at 1,313ft above sea level it is the highest railway tunnel in Great Britain) to a new terminus is planned for the future. Motive power is mainly steam and includes examples from Wales, Germany and South Africa including the most powerful locomotive built for this gauge, a 2-6-2+2-6-2 Garratt No.77 (currently being rebuilt). In recent years the mainstay has been *Graf Schwerin-Lowitz*, built by Arn Jung of Germany in 1908. Continental-style rolling stock, with end balconies, and a North American caboose have all been built in the company's well-equipped workshop at Pant, open for public viewing. A journey along the line starts at the

Right 0-6-2WT *Graf Schwerin-Lorwitz* at Pontsticill on the 1ft 11³/₄in gauge Brecon Mountain Railway *(Julian Holland)*

grand purpose-built station at Pant and follows a 600yd new alignment before reaching the former B&M trackbed. Disused quarries can be glimpsed from the train before it enters the Brecon Beacons National Park near Taf Fechan reservoir. At Pontsticill station the original signalbox can still be seen, although it is now a holiday cottage. The journey continues along the banks of the reservoir, with superb views of the Brecon Beacons, over rail obtained from various ammunition factories, until Dolygaer is reached. Passengers are not allowed to alight here and the train returns to Pontsticill where a stop is made.

Caerphilly Railway Centre

Caerphilly Business Park
Van Road
Caerphilly
Mid-Glamorgan

Tel: 01633 273182
Open: Sunday afternoons. Telephone for details of steaming days
Facilities: Car park, shop and refreshments (open days only)

Housed in the former Rhymney Railway's locomotive works at Caerphilly, the Centre was founded in 1973 and is home to locomotives and rolling stock from South Wales, including Taff Vale Railway 0-6-2 tank No. 28. A fully restored working signalbox from the Brecon & Merthyr Railway is also open to the public. Steam trains operate on certain open days along a short stretch of track within the site.

Conwy Valley Railway Museum

The Old Goods Yard
Betws-y-Coed
Gwynedd

Tel: 01690 710568
Open: Daily Easter to October
Facilities: Car park, refreshments, shop, miniature railway, picnic site, facilities for disabled

A railway museum, situated adjacent to BR's Conwy Valley station at Betws-y-Coed, that includes exhibits covering the whole railway scene and in particular North Wales. Included are Jack Nelson's intricate dioramas showing the railways in their heyday and a working model railway. In the grounds of the museum are a 1¼-mile long 7¼in gauge miniature steam railway, operating with American-style steam locomotives, and a 15in gauge electric tramway.

Corris Railway Museum

Corris Station Yard
Corris
Machynlleth
Powys SY20 9SH

Tel: 01654 761303
Open: April to September, excluding some Saturdays. Telephone for details
Facilities: Car park, refreshments, shop, facilities for disabled

Housed in former 2ft 3in gauge Corris Railway buildings this museum is devoted to many exhibits and photographs from that railway. Opened in 1859 to transport slate from the quarries around Corris to the main line at Machynlleth, this narrow gauge line was originally worked as a horse-tramway. Steam locomotives and passenger trains were later introduced and in 1930 the railway was taken over and worked by the GWR. Passenger traffic ceased at the end of 1930 and goods traffic in 1948. The museum contains a variety of historic wagons and the skeleton of an 1890s Corris Railway bogie carriage. A preservation group is currently working to re-open part of the line for passengers, of which ¾-mile of track from Corris Station yard has already been laid. Planning permission has been obtained for a further two miles southwards through the beautiful Esgairgeiliog Gorge. South of Corris the original engine shed at Maespoeth, built in 1878, has been restored and adapted to meet the current-day

Left 7¼in gauge Denver & Rio Grande 2-8-0 awaits departure at Conwy Valley Railway Museum *(Julian Holland)*

Right Early days in the restoration of the 2ft 3in gauge Corris Railway *(Richard S Greenhough)*

needs of the railway. Passenger services may start in 1996, but legal matters may delay this until 1997. Two diesels and a steam locomotive (under construction) form the motive power.

Fairbourne & Barmouth Steam Railway

Beach Road
Fairbourne
Gwynedd LL38 2PZ

Tel: 01341 250362
Route: Fairbourne to Porth Penrhyn (for Barmouth Ferry)
Length: 2½ miles
Gauge: 12¼in
Open: Daily Easter to end September
Facilities: Car park, refreshments, shop, driving experience courses

The Fairbourne & Barmouth Railway has had a very chequered history. Originally built as a 2ft gauge horse-drawn construction tramway in 1896 the line was eventually rebuilt to 15in gauge in 1916 by Narrow Gauge Railways, Bassett-Lowke's company, using miniature steam locomotives to convey passengers from Fairbourne, on the Cambrian Coast line, across sand dunes alongside the Mawddach estuary to Porth Penrhyn where trains connected with the ferry to Barmouth. After closure during World War II, following destruction by storms and military exercises, the line was re-opened in 1947 and enjoyed considerable success during the late 1960s and early 1970s. The line faced closure in 1984 but was bought by a new owner who regauged the line to 12¼in gauge in the winter of 1985/86 using half size (6in to 1ft) replica narrow gauge locomotives, adding a tunnel, signalboxes, workshop and restaurant. The line currently uses one diesel and four steam locomotives, including a scale version of the Darjeeling Himalayan Railway 0-4-0ST *Sherpa*, with a total of 28

Left Train bound for Blaenuau Ffestiniog passes Tan-y-Grisiau on the 1ft 11½in gauge Ffestiniog Railway *(AA Photo Library)*

coaches. In 1994 the railway was again put up for sale, with a new purchaser taking over in the Spring of 1995.

Ffestiniog Railway Company

Harbour Station
Porthmadog
Gwynedd LL49 9NF

Tel: 01766 512340/01766 514114 (talking timetable)
Route: Porthmadog (Harbour) to Blaenau Ffestiniog
Length: 13½ miles
Gauge: 1ft 11½in
Open: Daily late March to early November, limited winter service
Facilities: Car parks, shop, refreshments, picnic site, museum, facilities for disabled

Opened in 1836 as a horse-drawn and gravity tramway to take slate from the quarries at Blaenau Ffestiniog down to the harbour at Porthmadog, the Ffestiniog Railway was converted to steam power in 1865. Always independent, the Ffestiniog managed to keep operating through to 1946 although passenger services ceased in 1939. In 1951 an early railway preservation group was formed and the first length of line across the Cob to Boston Lodge was re-opened in 1955. In stages the line was reopened to Tan-y-Bwlch, Dduallt - where a spiral was built to take the railway at a higher level past the new hydro-electric reservoir - and finally to Blaenau Ffestiniog in May 1982. Here FR trains now run into a newly-built station adjacent to the BR Conwy Valley terminus, while at Minffordd passengers can make connection with the BR Cambrian Coast line. Original Victorian rolling stock and locomotives (dating from 1863), including the unique double Fairlies (introduced in 1872), have been beautifully restored at the company's Boston Lodge works. The latest project taking shape at the works is the construction of a replica of the Lynton & Barnstaple Railway locomotive *Lyd*. Carriages Nos. 15 and 16, introduced in 1873, were the first

true bogie coaches in Great Britain and were among the earliest iron-framed coaches in the world. A trip on the line affords the traveller wonderful views of Snowdonia as the train steadily climbs high above Porthmadog hugging the contours, round sharp curves, through tunnels and along ledges cut into the mountainside. The Ffestiniog Railway Museum, at Porthmadog Harbour Station, depicts the history of the line and includes the 1863-built 0-4-0 saddle and tender tank locomotive *Princess* and the famous hearse wagon as well as many other historic wagons.

Gloddfa Ganol Narrow Gauge Railway Centre

Gloddfa Ganol Slate Mine
Blaenau Ffestiniog
Gwynedd LL41 3NB

Tel: 01766 830664
Open: Monday to Friday Easter to October and some Sundays during holiday season
Facilities: Car park, museum

Situated in the world's largest slate mine is a museum of the slate industry, a restored quarry workshop with displays of slate cutting and a static collection of over 70 industrial narrow gauge steam and diesel locomotives.

Glyn Valley Tramway Group

Glyn Valley Hotel
Glyn Ceiriog
Nr Llangollen
Clwyd

Tel: 01691 718896 (Hotel), 0151 336 3569 (GVTG)
Open: During licensing hours
Facilities: Car park, refreshments

Housed in the Glyn Valley Hotel is a collection of photographs and ephemera of the Glyn Valley Tramway. Originally opened in 1873 as a horse and gravity worked slate tramway this 2ft 4½in gauge line was converted to steam haulage in 1888. The 8³/₄-mile route from Chirk along the picturesque valley of the River Ceiriog used tram-style steam locomotives until its final closure in 1935. Occasional 'Study Days' are held by the Group. These include lectures and trackbed walks.

Great Orme Tramway

Victoria Station
Church Walks
Llandudno
Gwynedd

Tel: 01492 876749/01492 870870
Route: Victoria Station to Great Orme Summit
Length: 1 mile 8 chains
Gauge: 3ft 6in
Open: Daily end March to end October
Facilities: Shop, refreshments, visitor centre

Opened in 1902, the Great Orme Tramway is the only cable-operated street tramway in Britain. Built to take passengers to the 679ft summit of the Great Orme, where there are magnificent views of Snowdonia, Anglesey and the Irish Sea, the line climbs gradients as steep as 1-in-4. The bottom terminus is at Victoria Station from which the line rises, firstly along the centre of the road, 400ft in 872yd. The upper section rises 150ft in 827yd along its own right of way. As the line is divided into two sections passengers have to change cars at the halfway point, where there is a central winding house. The original steam-driven winding drums were replaced by electricity in 1958. Four original tramcars survive, all 30ft long with end balconies and seating 48 people, and are equipped with radio-telephone links to the winding house. Future plans include building, by 1999, a new Half Way station with interpretative material showing the history of the tramway.

Gwili Steam Railway

Bronwydd Arms Station
Bronwydd Arms
Carmarthen
Dyfed SA33 6HT

Tel: 01267 230666
Route: Bronwydd Arms to Llwyfan Cerrig
Length: 1¹/₂ miles
Gauge: Standard
Open: April to October and Christmas period. Telephone for details
Facilities: Car park, shop, refreshments, picnic site, miniature railway (see p.75), facilities for disabled

The ex-GWR branch from Carmarthen to Aberystwyth, opened in 1860 as a broad gauge (7ft 0¹/₄in) line and was closed by BR to passengers in 1964 and to goods in 1973. In 1978 a preservation group had starting running services over a short length of track at Bronwydd Arms station three miles north of Carmarthen. By 1987 the line was extended to its present terminus at Llwyfan Cerrig, where there is a picnic site and 7¹/₄in gauge miniature railway (see p.75). The present railway company owns the eight miles of trackbed between Abergwili Junction, Carmarthen to Llanpumpsaint and the re-opening of this whole section along the picturesque Gwili valley is a long term project. The railway owns a large collection of mainly industrial steam and diesel locomotives and a wide variety of passenger and goods rolling stock, including an award-winning Taff Vale Railway coach, dating from 1891, which was fully restored after being found in a field in Herefordshire. Bronwydd Arms signalbox originally stood at Llandybie on the Central Wales Line and was bought in 1985 for use on the Gwili Railway. Dating from 1885, the 21-lever box is now fully restored and operates signals in the station area.

Left GWR 2-6-2T No. 4566 heads a train on the Gwili Railway *(AA Photo Library)*

Joys of Life Visitor Centre

Coed-y-Parc
Bethesda
Bangor
Gwynedd

Tel: 01248 602122
Open: School holidays only, Easter to August
Facilities: Car park, picnic site, nature reserve

The centre, situated in a 12-acre private park, houses several collections of railway memorabilia and models, and features a ³/₄-mile long 5in gauge, ground-level, working quarry railway. Construction started in 1982 and is very detailed, with stations, signalling, passing loops, cuttings, embankments, tunnel, bridges, level crossings and engine shed with turntable. The railway is situated in a very scenic and beautiful setting with flower beds, lawns, meadows, woodland and a mountain stream.

Llanberis Lake Railway

Gilfach Ddu
Llanberis
Gwynedd LL55 4TY

Tel: 01286 870549
Route: Gilfach Ddu (Llanberis) to Penllyn
Length: 2 miles
Gauge: 1ft 11¹/₂in
Open: March to October. Telephone for details
Facilities: Car park, refreshments, shop, picnic site, walks, facilities for disabled

The 4ft gauge Padarn Railway was opened in 1843 to transport slate from the quarries at Llanberis to Port Dinorwic along the north shore of Llyn Padarn. Both the port and the railway were owned by the Dinorwic Quarry company, who also operated a system of 1ft 10³/₄in lines within their quarries. Initially the line was a horse-worked tramway but steam power was soon introduced in 1848. The decline in the slate industry eventually caused the closure of the line in 1961 but in 1970 work began on building a

The Llanberis Lake Railway runs alongside Llyn Padarn with views of Snowdon *(Llanberis Lake Railway)*

narrow gauge tourist railway along part of the trackbed. By 1972 the present route from Llanberis to Penllyn was complete and open to passengers. The line is run by three Hunslet 0-4-0 steam locomotives that originally worked in the nearby Dinorwic quarries and passengers are carried in both open and closed carriages which were all built in the railway's workshop. A journey along the line gives splendid views across the lake to Snowdon and the massive hydro-electric plant that is inside the nearby mountain on the same side of the lake as the railway. The Welsh Slate Museum (see p.82), situated near the station at Gilfach Ddu, which illustrates the history of the local slate industry, is well worth a visit.

Llangollen Railway

Llangollen Station
Abbey Road
Llangollen
Clwyd LL20 8SN

Tel: 01978 860979/01978 890951 (talking timetable)
Route: Llangollen to Glyndyfrdwy (currently being extended to Carrog)
Length: 5¹/₄ miles
Gauge: Standard
Open: February to December. Telephone for details
Facilities: Shop, refreshments, model railway, picnic site, combined rail/canal trips, Wine & Dine train, funeral train, facilities for disabled

Opened in 1865 as the Llangollen & Corwen Railway this line became part of the GWR route from Ruabon to Barmouth before eventually being closed by BR in 1965. A preservation group moved into Llangollen, its station attractively situated on the north bank of the River Dee, in 1975 with the ultimate goal of re-opening the line as far as Corwen. Since then much progress has been made, with Berwyn being reached in 1985, Deeside Halt in 1990 and Glyndyfrdwy in 1992. Work is now progressing towards Corwen with the section to Carrog being due for re-opening in Easter 1996. The two major engineering features of the line are the bridge over the River Dee to the west of Llangollen and the 689yd single bore tunnel near Berwyn. A journey along the line, the only preserved standard gauge example in North Wales, gives passengers wonderful views of the Dee Valley as the train climbs high above the river and parallels the A5 trunk road. Berwyn station with its black and white timbered building and tea room is located in a magnificent position overlooking the River Dee. A large collection of steam, including many ex-GWR examples, and diesel locomotives maintain passenger services on the line, which is also a frequent host to visiting main line engines from other preserved railways. A new locomotive shed was opened at Llangollen in November 1995 and this will provide accommodation for up to ten locomotives and a carriage restoration section. The 'Berwyn Belle' Wine & Dine train operates on some Saturday evenings and Sunday lunchtimes and prospective customers should contact Bryn Derwen Hotel (Tel. 01978 860583).

Llechwedd Slate Caverns

Blaenau Ffestiniog
Gwynedd LL41 3NB

Tel: 01766 830306
Open: Daily except Christmas and New Year
Facilities: Car park, refreshments, shop

An underground inclined railway takes visitors down to explore the lower reaches of this slate mine. Exhibits and demonstrations illustrate the fascinating history of this once-important local industry. Passengers can also travel on the 1846 2ft gauge Miner's Tramway underground line, opened to the public in 1972, with trains pulled by a battery-electric locomotive. These locomotives were made by British Electric Vehicles, of Southport, and were introduced to Llechwedd in 1921 to replace horses. The 3ft gauge Deep Mine railway is the steepest operating passenger railway in Britain with a gradient of 1-in-1.8 and passengers travel in a specially made 24-seat car. A large collection of narrow gauge rolling stock is on display, including 2ft gauge L&NWR and GWR stock specially made for use in the slate quarries of Blaenau Ffestiniog.

Llwyfan Cerrig Miniature Railway

Llwyfan Cerrig Station (Gwili Railway)
Nr Carmarthen
Dyfed

Tel: 01267 230666
Route: Within site of Llwyfan Cerrig station on Gwili Railway (see p.72)
Length: 200yd
Gauge: 7^1/$_4$in
Open: As Gwili Railway
Facilities: Picnic site, quarry walk

This miniature railway opened in 1993 as an added attraction for Gwili Railway passengers. The route takes trains through a wooded valley alongside the Gwili Railway trackbed. However this is likely to be re-opened in the near future and the miniature line will then be relocated. Trains are operated by *Jason*, a modified steam Romulus design, and *Michael*, a freelance petrol hydraulic. There is no access to Llwyfan Cerrig station other than by travelling on the Gwili Railway.

Narrow Gauge Railway Museum

Wharf Station
Tywyn
Gwynedd LL36 9EY

Tel: 01654 710472
Open: Easter to October
Facilities: See Talyllyn Railway (p.78)

A comprehensive collection of British narrow gauge locomotives, rolling stock and artefacts mainly relating to the Welsh slate industry. The museum is situated at the Talyllyn Railway's Wharf Station in Tywyn. Locomotives on display include *Jubilee 1897* together with others from Welsh slate quarries, a Dublin brewery, a Dundee gas works and a Manchester Locomotive Works.

Narrower Gauge Railway

Eirias Park
Colwyn Bay
Clwyd

Route: Within grounds of Eirias Park
Length: ^{1}/$_4$ mile
Gauge: 10^1/$_4$in
Open: Easter, then weekends to Spring bank holiday, then daily until mid September
Facilities: Car park, refreshments, picnic site, leisure centre

From 1907 to 1956 Colwyn Bay was linked to Llandudno by a 3ft 6in gauge electric tramway and its route passed Eirias Park. There have also been three different 10^1/$_4$in gauge miniature railways in the Colwyn Bay area. The current line operates in 50 acres of parkland on the coast and has been developed since 1985. Public operations in the park started in 1991 and the present circuit was first used in 1992. The narrow gauge type locomotives include 2-4-4 tank *Lynton* and two battery electric engines. Passenger coaches are four-wheeled, semi-enclosed with end balconies, and fitted with vacuum brakes. Extensions to the present circuit are planned for the future.

Opposite GWR 'Manor' class 4-6-0 No. 7822 *Foxcote Manor* pauses at Berwyn station on the Llangollen Railway *(Julian Holland)*

The Old Station

Tintern Station
Tintern
Nr Chepstow
Gwent NP6 7NX

Tel: 01291 689566
Open: April to early November
Facilities: Car park, picnic site, refreshments, railway exhibition, miniature railway, walks

This station and signalbox are situated on the former Chepstow to Monmouth branch line, opened in 1876 by the Wye Valley Railway, amalgamated with the GWR in 1905 and completely closed by BR in 1964. The restored station building and signalbox were opened in 1975 as an information centre with a display of local railway history. Two restored railway coaches are also on site – a 1935 GWR corridor coach used as an information and sales area, and a 1955 BR example used as a lecture area for schools. On pre-arranged days throughout the season a passenger-carrying $7^{1}/_{4}$in gauge steam hauled miniature railway is in operation along part of the old trackbed.

Penrhyn Castle Industrial Railway Museum

Penrhyn Castle
Llandegai
Nr Bangor
Gwynedd

Tel: 01248 353084
Open: April to October
Facilities: Car park, shop, refreshments, facilities for disabled

Situated in the former stables of this National Trust property is a large collection of industrial steam locomotives and rolling stock, both standard and narrow gauge, including exhibits from the Dinorwic Quarry and the Padarn and Penrhyn Railways. The oldest locomotive in the collection is the 4ft gauge Padarn Railway 0-4-0

Fire Queen built in 1848. There is also a display of railway signs and models.

Pontypool & Blaenavon Railway

Nr Big Pit Mining Museum
Blaenavon
Gwent

Tel: 01495 792263
Route: Furnace Sidings to Whistle Inn
Length: $^{3}/_{4}$ mile
Gauge: Standard
Open: Sundays Easter to end August and December. Telephone for details
Facilities: Car park, refreshments, shop

The original plan was to re-open the eight miles of the former London & North Western Railway's branch between Pontypool and Blaenavon, fully opened in 1877, closed to passengers in 1941 and which was completely closed by BR in 1980. Services began in 1983 but problems have been encountered and activity is currently restricted to steam and diesel operations between Furnace Sidings and Whistle Inn within the present site, which is centred around the Big Pit Mining Museum. The line runs by a newly-established country park that has been developed from ex-colliery waste sites, and part of the line currently operated runs up to 1,200ft above sea level. The railway plans to develop in stages over the next few years until it extends from Abersychan through to Brynmawr, a distance of eight miles. When the railway reaches Waenavon it will re-open the station that, at 1,400ft above sea level, was the highest standard gauge station in England and Wales. The first stage will see the line extended $^{1}/_{2}$-mile southwards to a platform near the Big Pit Mining Museum.

Rhiw Valley Railway

Lower House Farm
Manafon
Welshpool
Powys SY21 8BJ

Route: Within site
Length: $1^{1}/_{4}$ miles
Gauge: 15in
Open: Once or twice a year for charity days – see local press

A private railway that runs through fields with two gated crossings has been kept going by the widow of its builder, and is open to the public only at selected times. Motive power is provided by steam 2-6-2 tank locomotive *Powys* built by Severn Lamb and a freelance design diesel, and passengers ride in four-wheeled carriages with longitudinal 'sofa' seats.

Rhyl Miniature Railway

Marine Lake
Rhyl
Clwyd

Route: Around Marine Lake
Length: 1 mile
Gauge: 15in
Open: During July and August

This typical seaside miniature railway takes passengers on a route around the perimeter of the Marine Lake at Rhyl, and on its southern shore parallels the North Wales Coast main line, where the locomotive shed is situated. Motive power includes 'Atlantic' 4-4-2 steam locomotive *Joan* built by Barnes.

Snowdon Mountain Railway

Llanberis
Nr Caernarfon
Gwynedd LL55 4TY

Tel: 01286 870223
Route: Llanberis to Snowdon Summit
Length: $4^{3}/_{4}$ miles
Gauge: 2ft $7^{5}/_{8}$in

Right Swiss-built 0-4-2T No. 6 *Padarn* takes on water on the rack and pinion Snowdon Mountain Railway *(AA Photo Library)*

Open: Mid march to end October depending on weather conditions
Facilities: Car park, shop, refreshments

Britain's only public rack and pinion mountain railway, with its unique gauge, takes passengers to the 3,560ft summit of the highest mountain in Wales from where, on clear days, there are spectacular views of Snowdonia and the Irish Sea. The line opened in 1896 but was closed on the same day after a fatal accident, the only one known on the line. It was re-opened in April 1899 and until 1986 all trains were steam-hauled using the Swiss-built locomotives, with their sloping boilers, some of which date back to the building of the line. Carriages are positioned, uncoupled, on the uphill side of the locomotive and have independent braking systems. Trains are restricted to a speed limit of 5mph on the line where gradients as severe as 1-in-5 can be encountered. Four Hunslet-built diesel hydraulic locomotives were introduced in 1986 as an economy measure but the seven 0-4-2 (the continental nomenclature would be 0-2-1T) steam locos, four of which are now over 100 years old, are still in constant use. These are numbered 2 to 8 (No.1 being involved in the accident on opening day) and are named *Enid*, *Yr Wyddfa*, *Snowdon*, *Moel Siabod*, *Padarn*, *Ralph* and *Eryri*. In late 1995 three diesel electric railcars, capable of multiple unit working, were undergoing commissioning trials and by October had started working a few revenue-earning trains. Passengers are advised that train services can be restricted by bad weather conditions, especially during the beginning and end of the operating season.

Swansea Maritime & Industrial Museum

Museum Square
Maritime Quarter
Swansea SA1 1SN

Tel: 01792 650351
Open: Tuesdays to Sundays, closed Mondays, 1st Jan and 24th-26th December
Facilities: Car park, shop, facilities for disabled

Exhibits from Swansea's maritime, industrial and transport history are displayed in this museum. Former dock sidings next to the Museum are occasionally used to operate some of the railway items. On view is a Peckett 0-6-0T dating from 1916, a restored Swansea City tram and Mumbles Railway tramcar No. 15, the only surviving item from that railway.

Swansea Vale Railway

Six Pit Junction
Nant-y-Ffin Road
Llansamlet
Swansea

Tel: 01792 653615
Route: Six Pit Junction to Cwm
Length: ²/₃ mile
Gauge: Standard
Open: April to October and December. Telephone for steaming days
Facilities: Car park, shop, steam driving courses

Originally a horse-drawn tramroad built in 1816, later rebuilt from 1845 by the Swansea Vale Railway Company. Passenger services commenced between Swansea and Pontardawe in 1860 and to Brynamman in 1868. The Midland Railway acquired the line in 1874 and eventually through services between Swansea (St Thomas) and Brecon, Hereford and Birmingham were introduced. After nationalisation passenger services were withdrawn in 1950 and a gradual piecemeal closure ensued. A preservation group was set up in 1980 to preserve part of the route but progress has been slow and the current extent of the line is the short distance from Six Pit Junction to Llansamlet. Six Pit Junction lies within the new area of Swansea Enterprise Park at Llansamlet and the restored section of railway passes under the main Swansea to Paddington main line before entering a Forest Park. Work is progressing to double the present length to 1¹/₂ miles with a proposed station at Cwm Halt and restoration of Upper Bank station. When opened to the public Upper Bank station will be the nucleus of the railway with a heritage centre and

restored Midland Railway features. Peckett 0-4-0 tank No. 1345, built in 1914, and a diesel multiple unit are currently operating services. Several other steam and diesel locomotives, including ex-GWR 0-6-0 pannier tank No. 9642 and ex-GWR 2-8-0 tank No. 4270, are currently being restored or awaiting restoration.

Talyllyn Railway

Wharf Station
Tywyn
Gwynedd LL36 9EY

Tel: 01654 710472
Route: Tywyn (Wharf) to Nant Gwernol
Length: 7¹/₂ miles
Gauge: 2ft 3in
Open: Daily April to October and Christmas period
Facilities: Car park, refreshments, shop, picnic site, museum (see p.75), facilities for disabled

Opened in 1866 to carry slate from the quarries above Nant Gwernol to Tywyn this scenic narrow gauge railway has never actually closed. When the slate quarry closed in 1946 the owner, Sir Henry Haydn Jones, managed to keep the railway running, but with little or no maintenance the line was in a very run-down state by the time of his death in 1950. However a group of volunteers saved it from imminent closure by taking over the running of the line to Abergynolwyn, thus making it the world's first successful railway preservation scheme. In 1976 the Preservation Society reopened the ³/₄-mile section of mineral line from Abergynolwyn to Nant Gwernol at the foot of the first incline that led to the quarry. Trains are still hauled by some of the original and beautifully preserved Talyllyn Railway locomotives, over 130 years old, and four-wheeled coaches are used as well as more recent additions with one from the defunct Corris Railway (see p.68). Locomotives, including three diesels, are numbered 1 to 9 and are named *Talyllyn* (0-4-2 saddle tank built 1865), *Dolgoch* (0-4-0 well tank built 1866), *Sir Haydn* (0-4-2 saddle tank built 1878), *Edward Thomas* (0-4-2 saddle tank built 1921), *Midlander* (diesel mechanical built 1940), *Douglas* (0-4-0 well tank built 1918), *Tom Rolt* (0-4-2 tank built 1949), *Merseysider* (diesel hydraulic built 1964) and *Alf* (diesel mechanical built 1950). The railway's workshop at Pendre has constructed bogie coaches and a new steam engine. A journey on the line today evokes all the atmosphere of a Victorian narrow gauge railway as the train slowly climbs along the wooded side of the valley of the Afon Fathew, affording panoramic views of Dolgoch Falls and the Welsh mountains.

Teifi Valley Railway

Henllan Station
Nr Newcastle Emlyn
Dyfed SA44 5TD

Tel: 01559 371077
Route: Henllan to Pontprenshitw
Length: 1¹/₂ miles
Gauge: 2ft
Open: Easter to October and December.
Telephone for details
Facilities: Car park, refreshments, shop, GWR museum and library, children's play area, woodland walks, facilities for disabled

Situated on the trackbed of the former GWR branch line from Pencader to Newcastle Emlyn, opened in 1895 and closed by BR in 1972, the narrow gauge Teifi Valley Railway began running trains in 1985. In 1990 the line was extended to Pontprenshitw with the long term aim of reaching Newcastle Emlyn and Llandyssul, a distance of six miles. Trains are operated by steam, including Hunslet 0-4-0 tank *Alan George*, built in 1894, and industrial diesel locomotives that originally worked in the slate quarries of North Wales. Passengers are carried in recreated Victorian carriages.

Right 0-4-2ST No. 1 *Talyllyn*, built in 1865, stands at Nant Gwernol station on the Talyllyn Railway *(Julian Holland)*

GWR 2-6-2T No. 9 *Prince of Wales* at Devil's Bridge station on the Vale of Rheidol Railway *(Julian Holland)*

Vale of Rheidol Light Railway

Park Avenue
Aberystwyth
Dyfed SY23 1PG

Tel: 01970 625819
Route: Aberystwyth to Devil's Bridge
Length: 11¾ miles
Gauge: 1ft 11¾in
Open: April to October. Telephone for details
Facilities: Car park, refreshments, shop

The Vale of Rheidol Light Railway was opened in 1902 as a narrow gauge line to serve leadmines, the timber industry and tourism. In 1913 the railway was amalgamated with its bigger neighbour, Cambrian Railways, which in turn was taken into the GWR empire in 1922. The GWR then virtually rebuilt the line, scrapped two of the original locomotives, rebuilt one and built two new ones. These three 2-6-2T locomotives, No. 7 *Owain Glyndwr*, No. 8 *Llywelyn* and No. 9 *Prince of Wales* are still working on the line although they have now all been converted to oil-burning. Goods traffic ceased in 1920, winter passenger services in 1931, and from then on the railway had to earn its living purely from tourism. Following temporary closure during World War II the railway was nationalised in 1948, unlike its near neighbour the Talyllyn Railway (see p.78), eventually becoming the only BR operated steam line in 1968. In 1989 BR controversially sold the whole operation to the Brecon Mountain Railway (see p.66) who are now running it. Trains now run from part of the mainline terminus at Aberystwyth passing the former GWR engine shed which now houses VOR locomotives and rolling stock. The Afon Rheidol is soon crossed on a newly reconstructed bridge and the railway begins to climb, gradually at first, up the southern side of the valley before taking water at the intermediate station of Nantyronen. The gradients soon become steeper with the line winding its way up a ledge cut into the hillside and after pausing at the crossing point at Aberffrwd passengers are treated to magnificent views of the river far below. The final approach to the terminus at Devil's Bridge is a continous 1-in-50 gradient with numerous sharp curves, and the entrance to the station, 639ft above sea level, is through a deep rock cutting. Within walking distance from the station are the famous beauty spots of Mynach Falls, Devil's Punchbowl and Jacob's Ladder.

Welsh Highland Railway

Gelert's Farm Works
Madoc Street West
Porthmadog
Gwynedd LL49 9DY

Tel: 01766 513402
Route: Porthmadog to Pen-y-Mount
Length: ¾ mile
Gauge: 1ft 11½in
Open: Easter to October. Telephone for details
Facilities: Car park, shop, refreshments, museum, picnic site, facilities for disabled

The Welsh Highland Railway originated as the North Wales Narrow Gauge Railway Company in 1877 and was acquired by the Welsh Highland Railway in 1923. In 1934 the WHR was leased to its neighbour, the Festiniog Railway. The line, at 22 miles in length being the longest narrow gauge railway in Wales, ran from Porthmadog to Dinas Junction via the Pass of Aberglaslyn and Beddgelert through the heart of Snowdonia, but was not a commercial success and finally closed in 1937. Track was lifted in 1941 and in 1964 a preservation group was formed to re-open the

Right Hunslet 2-6-2T *Russell* at Porthmadog on the Welsh Highland Railway *(Julian Holland)*

line. Since 1980 the Welsh Highland Light Railway (1964) Ltd has been operating passenger services over a short length of track from Porthmadog. Because the rest of the trackbed was still in the hands of the Official Receiver, plans to re-open the line completely have involved lengthy litigation and argument with the neighbouring Festiniog Railway who also wanted to take over the project. A recent High Court action has decided that the Festiniog Railway can rebuild and operate the line (see below). However the WHR(1964) Ltd hopes that it can now become part of the project and extend its own operation. The railway currently owns and operates several steam locomotives, notably 2-6-2T *Russell* built by Hunslet in 1906 for the North Wales Narrow Gauge Railway, in addition to a large fleet of industrial narrow gauge diesels, which are all housed in the railway's workshop at Gelert's Farm.

Note In 1995 the Festiniog Railway was given permission to rebuild the former Welsh Highland Railway. An award of £4.3 million from the national lottery millennium fund may greatly speed up the process of rebuilding the line. The first section from Caernarfon to Dinas is scheduled for opening in 1997 and the next section to Rhyd Ddu by 1999. The FR has already purchased two powerful oil-fired Garratts, for use on the new line, from the Alfred County Railway in South Africa, and plans to build a fleet of 40 new coaches for passenger services. Planning permission was granted in December 1995 for the reconstruction of the first three miles from Caernarfon to Dinas Junction.

Welshpool & Llanfair Light Railway

The Station
Llanfair Caereinion
Powys SY21 0SF

Tel: 01938 810441
Route: Llanfair Caereinion to Welshpool (Raven Square)
Length: 8 miles

Gauge: 2ft 6in
Open: Easter to October. Telephone for details
Facilities: Car parks, shop, refreshments, picnic site, facilities for disabled

The Welshpool & Llanfair, opened in 1903, was one of the first railways built under the Light Railways Act of 1896. It has some of the steepest gradients (max. 1-in-24) on an adhesion railway in Britain, and was built to carry general merchandise, coal, timber and livestock between farms in the Banwy valley and the local market town of Welshpool. Until closure W&L trains ran through the back streets of the town to an interchange with the Cambrian Railways standard gauge station. From the beginning the railway was run by the Cambrian until it was absorbed into the GWR in 1922. The last passenger train ran in 1931 but goods traffic continued, and in 1948 the line became part of the nationalised British Railways. BR closed the line in 1956 but a preservation group stepped in and re-opened the first section to passengers in 1963. The line, following the delightful Banwy valley from Llanfair Caereinion, now ends at the new Raven Square station on the west side of Welshpool, using buildings from the 1863 Eardisley station. The two original Beyer Peacock locomotives, *The Earl* and *Countess*, still work on the line alongside steam engines from Austria, Finland, Sierra Leone and Antigua and continental-style balcony carriages from Austria and bogie coaches from Sierra Leone.

Welsh Industrial & Maritime Museum

Bute Street
Cardiff CF1 6AN

Tel: 01222 481919
Open: Tuesdays to Saturdays, Sunday afternoons and bank holiday Mondays. Closed Christmas and New Year
Facilities: Car park, miniature railway

A museum opened in 1971 that depicts the history of transport and industry in Wales

including a large model of the Taff Vale Railway's West Yard Locomotive Works and a full-scale working replica of *Pen-y-Daren*, the 4ft 2in gauge locomotive built by Trevithick in 1804 for the Dowlais ironworks. On the first Saturday of spring and in summer months the museum's collection of engines are driven by steam, giving a taste of 19th century industrial atmosphere. Other exhibits include Cambrian and Taff Vale Railway carriages. A 10$\frac{1}{4}$in gauge passenger carrying miniature railway encircles the site.

Welsh Slate Museum

Padarn Country Park
Llanberis
Gwynedd LL55 4TY

Tel: 01286 870630
Open: Daily April to September, weekdays only in March and October
Facilities: Car park, shop, facilities for disabled

The workshops, built in 1870, that now house the museum remain much as they were when the vast Dinorwic slate quarry, sited alongside, was still being worked. Included in the museum are slate splitting demonstrations, an enormous water-wheel, brass casting and exhibitions relating to the slate industry. Of interest to railway enthusiasts is a 0-4-0 61cm gauge steam locomotive *Una*, built in 1905 by Hunslet. It is now in full working order and is regularly steamed during summer months. Also on display is a diesel Simplex shunter built in 1961, a large steam crane, two velocipedes and various historic slate wagons. The narrow gauge Llanberis Lake Railway (see p.73) is situated adjacent to the museum.

Right Beyer Peacock 0-6-0T No. 823 *Countess* hauls a charter freight train on the Welshpool & Llanfair Railway, September 30 1995 *(Mike Esau)*

The Midlands and East Anglia

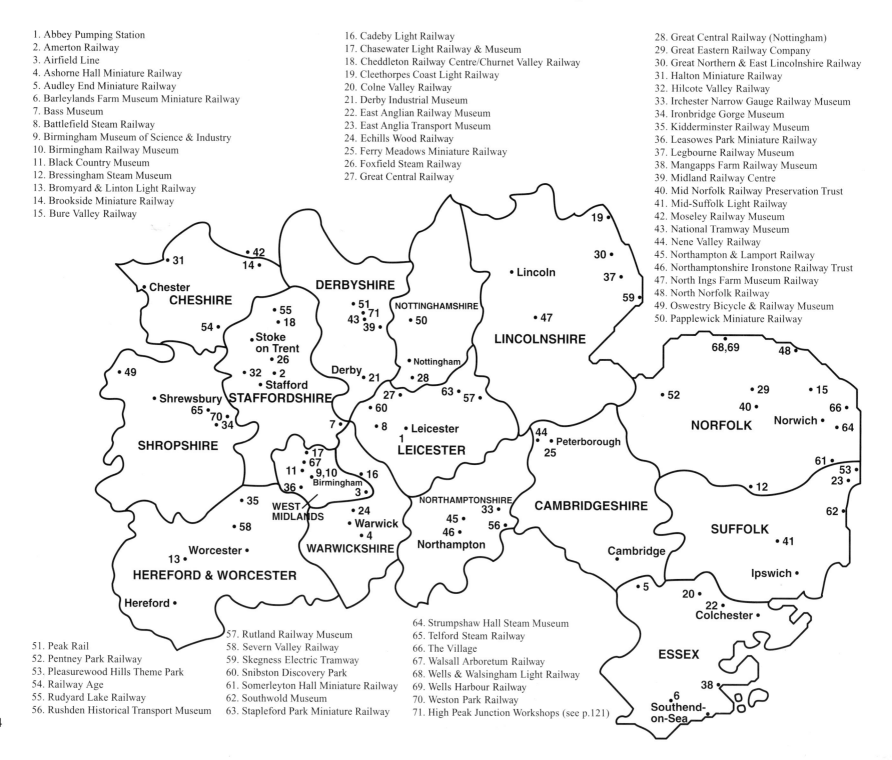

Abbey Pumping Station

Corporation Road
Leicester LE4 5PX

Tel: 0116 2661330
Route: Within site of museum
Length: 300yd
Gauge: 2ft
Open: Mondays to Saturdays and Sunday
afternoons. Railway operates on certain Sundays.
Telephone for details
Facilities: Car park, museum, shop, facilities for
disabled

A former sewage pumping station now houses a
museum that includes the four original Gimsons
beam engines built in 1891, and stationary steam
engines. Two of the beam engines operate on
special open days. On view is a narrow gauge
railway operated by industrial diesel and petrol
locomotives, that demonstrates how the line was
originally used to move solid sewage from the
screens to a tip. Visiting steam locomotives
operate on steaming days. Passengers are not
carried on the trains. Future plans include laying
an old brick yard traverser.

Amerton Railway

Amerton Working Farm
Stowe-by-Chartley
Stafford
Staffs ST18 0LA

Tel: 01785 284388
Route: Within site of working farm
Length: 1/4 mile
Gauge: 2ft
Open: Sundays from end March to early October.
Saturdays Easter to August Bank Holiday and
Bank Holiday Mondays
Facilities: Car park, refreshments, craft centre,
garden centre

The construction of the Amerton Railway was
started on a greenfield site in 1990 by volunteers
of the Staffordshire Narrow Gauge Railway

Society. The present route was opened in 1992.
Passenger trains consist of two modified Baguley
toast-rack coaches and a home-made brakevan.
Operating locomotives include Bagnall steam
tank *Isabel*, built in Stafford in 1897 (operates
Sundays and bank holidays) and steam outline
diesel *Dreadnought* (operates Saturdays). Several
others are on display and used on permanent way
duties. Future plans include completing the route
into a mile-long circular line and forming a
museum of Staffordshire-built narrow gauge
railway items. Restoration of an ex-Great
Northern Railway wooden waiting room from
Stowe-by-Chartley station is an imminent project.

Airfield Line (formerly Coventry Steam Railway Centre)

Coventry Airport
Rowley Road
Coventry
Warwickshire

Tel: 01455 634373/01455 635440 (evenings only)
Route: Within boundary of Coventry Airport
Length: 200yd
Gauge: Standard
Open: Sundays and bank holidays from Easter to
October. Telephone for details
Facilities: Car park, refreshments

Originally known as the Coventry Steam Railway
Centre which opened in 1986 on a greenfield site
within the boundary of Coventry Airport. It is run
by a combination of the operating company and
the supporting 1857 Society. The latter was
originally formed to restore Hudswell Clarke
0-6-0 saddle tank No. 1857 as far back as 1975.
After many years of fruitless searching for a suitable
home, planning permission for the current six-acre
site was granted by Warwick District Council in
1983. After many years of ups and downs the
society's aim is to run passenger shuttles over a
1/3-mile length of track. Tracklaying started in the
late 1980s and is currently about 200yd long.
Locomotives include of the still unrestored
No. 1857, diesel electric 0-4-0 *Mazda*, which is
fully restored and in running condition, as well as

another unrestored 0-4-0 Andrew Barclay tank
and several diesels. An interesting item, currently
being restored to working order, is a Carrick &
Wardale steam crane built in 1919, which was
previously languishing on the North Norfolk
Railway. A London & North Western Railway
waiting shelter, built in 1878, from Welford &
Kilworth station, and a Midland Railway
signalbox from Little Bowden Junction, have
been re-erected and restored on the site.

Ashorne Hall Miniature Railway

Ashorne Hill
Nr Warwick
Warwickshire CV33 9QN

Tel: 01926 651444
Route: In grounds of Ashorne Hall
Length: 1 mile
Gauge: 12 1/4 in
Open: Sundays from Palm Sunday to first Sunday
in November, Saturdays July and August
Facilities: Car park, refreshments, nickelodeon
collection

Ashorne Hall is the home of the famous
nickelodeon collection with a spectacular cinema
organ show. A half-size (6in to 1ft) narrow gauge
steam railway, running on a steeply-graded 12 1/4 in
gauge track, with two period stations and first
class carriages, takes passengers through five
acres of gardens and woods in this picturesque
setting. Motive power consists of a 2-4-2 narrow
gauge steam locomotive and a Coventry Climax-
driven petrol engine.

Audley End Miniature Railway

Audley End Estate Office
Blunicketts
Wendens Ambo
Saffron Walden
Essex CB11 4JL

Tel: 01799 41354/01799 41956
Route: Return loop in grounds of Audley End
House

85

Length: 1½ miles
Gauge: 10¼in
Open: Daily during Easter week and summer school holidays, weekend afternoons mid March to mid October
Facilities: Car park

Lord Braybrooke, owner of Audley End House, began building this miniature railway in 1963 on a site within the grounds of the house. The first section of line was opened by Stirling Moss in 1964 with trains being operated by one steam and one diesel locomotive. The line was extended to its present layout, an extended return loop, in 1979. A journey on the line, which is fully signalled, takes passengers across bridges over the Rivers Fulfen and Cam and through a tunnel before passing along the bank of the latter river. Locomotives on the roster include a one-third scale model weighing three tons of the Denver & Rio Grande Railroad 2-8-2 *Sara Lucy*, a Great Northern Railway Ivatt 'Atlantic' 4-4-2, two American-style 2-6-2s and a 'Western' class diesel, No. 1011 *Western Thunderer*.

Barleylands Farm Museum Miniature Railway

Barleylands Road
Billericay
Essex

Tel: 01268 282090/01268 532253
Route: Within site of museum
Length: 900yd
Gauge: 7¼in
Open: Summer Sundays weather permitting. Groups by prior arrangement
Facilities: Car park, refreshments, museum

With the exception of one locomotive the whole railway came from the North Benfleet miniature railway owned by the late Mr R Watson, purchased by Mr P Philpot in 1988. The entire railway was moved to Barleylands Farm and the first section opened in 1989. The line starts at the museum, where the engine shed is located, runs for about 400yd turning through 180° to Littlewood Junction where the engine runs round

the train, and then runs for some 500yd mainly downhill to the exit from the boot fair field where there is a small station and run-round loop. The four ex-North Benfleet locomotives are all ⅛ full size and include 4-6-2 *Britannia*, 2-10-0 *Black Prince*, 2-6-0 *Vulcan* and 4-4-2 tank *Maid of Benfleet*. A further locomotive, narrow gauge 0-6-2 tank *Gowrie* was added to the roster in 1994.

Bass Museum

Horninglow Street
Burton-on-Trent
Staffs DE14 1YQ

Tel: 01283 511000
Open: Daily except Christmas and New Year
Facilities: Car park, shop, refreshments

This museum depicts the history of brewing, for which Burton-on-Trent is famed, and exhibits include an 'N' gauge model of Bass & Co's extensive railway system circa 1921. Also on display is a Neilson-Reid saddle tank built in 1904, which was used on the brewery's private railway until the 1960s, and a 1926 Planet diesel shunter which was operated by Worthington's brewery. Visitors can also see a directors' coach that was originally built for the Manchester Ship Canal Company, bought by Bass in 1880 and used on the company's railway network until the 1960s.

Battlefield Steam Railway

Shackerstone Railway Station
Shackerstone
Leicestershire CV13 6NW

Tel: 01827 880754
Route: Shackerstone to Shenton
Length: 4¾ miles

Left The 'N' gauge model of the Bass Brewery rail system at the Bass Museum *(Bass Museum)*
Right 0-6-0ST No. 4 takes on water on the Battlefield Line in 1994 *(AA Photo Library)*

Gauge: Standard
Open: Steam – Sundays Easter to October, Saturdays May to September, Wednesdays June to August, Santa Specials in December; Diesel – March to November
Facilities: Car park, shop, refreshments, museum, canal-side picnic site, Wine & Dine train

The Battlefield Line, named after the nearby site of the Battle of Bosworth (1485), is situated on the old LNW & Midland Joint Railway line between Nuneaton and Coalville, opened in 1873, closed to passengers in 1931 and finally closed by BR in 1968. A preservation group took over in 1969 and has recently extended the line from Market Bosworth to Shenton. A large collection of diesel multiple units and industrial steam and diesel locomotives are used on this typical English rural railway, which runs through delightful countryside alongside the Ashby Canal which originally opened in 1804. Steam locomotives include No. 3 *Lamport* and No. 4 built by Robert Stephenson -Hawthorn. Various ex-BR steam locomotives visit the line, including 'Jubilee' class 4-6-0 *Bahamas* in the summer of 1996. The 'Tudor Rose' dining train runs on the third Sunday of each month and the Bosworth Battlefield Country Park can be reached on foot from Shenton station, this building being originally situated at Leicester Humberstone Road.

Birmingham Museum of Science & Industry

Newhall Street
Birmingham B3 1RZ

Tel: 0121 235 1661
Open: All year, Mondays to Saturdays and Sunday afternoons. Closed Christmas and New Year
Facilities: Car park, shop, refreshments, facilities for disabled

This large museum opened in 1951 and has expanded ever since. A wide range of exhibits includes the world's oldest working steam engine by James Watt, built in 1779, Murdock's steam vehicle of 1784 and machine tools and transport sections. Four historic steam railway locomotives on display are standard gauge LMS 'Coronation' class 4-6-2 No. 46235 *City of Birmingham* (built 1939), 2ft 8in gauge 0-6-0 well tank *Secundus* (built 1874), and 2ft gauge 0-4-0 saddle tanks *Leonard* (built 1919) and *Lorna Doone* (built 1922).

Birmingham Railway Museum

670 Warwick Road
Tyseley
Birmingham B11 2HL

Tel: 0121 707 4696
Open: Daily except Christmas and New Year
Facilities: Car park, shop, refreshments, footplate driving experience

A large collection of engines and rolling stock are based in the former GWR repair shop at Tyseley. The site is fully equipped for locomotive preservation and overhaul and is home to seven GWR locomotives, including three 'Castles' and a 'Hall', two LMS locomotives (a 'Jubilee' and a 'Royal Scot'), three BR diesels and five industrial locomotives. A varied collection of rolling stock includes a travelling post office and a steam crane. The museum also arranges driving and firing lessons on steam locomotives, which operate along the 600yd of track within the site.

Black Country Museum

Tipton Road
Dudley
West Midlands

Tel: 0121 557 9643
Open: Daily March to October, Wednesdays to Sundays November to February
Facilities: Car park, shop, museum, canal boat trips

This open air museum, situated next to the northern end of the Dudley Canal Tunnel, is devoted to exhibits from the age of the industrial revolution in this part of the Midlands, commonly known as 'The Black Country'. The 26-acre museum contains canal boats, a boatyard, bakery, 19th century houses, a chainmaking shop, a colliery steam winding engine, working replica of the 1712 Newcomen pumping engine and an underground mining exhibition. All of these attractions can be visited in a 1920s tramcar travelling on a 3ft 6in gauge electric tramway which crosses the site.

Bressingham Steam Museum

Bressingham Hall
Diss
Norfolk IP22 2AB

Tel: 01379 687386/01379 687382
Open: Daily April to September
Facilities: Car park, shop, restaurant, picnic sites, gardens, plant centre, traction engine museum, miniature, narrow and standard gauge railways, facilities for disabled

Bressingham is not only known for its extensive steam museum but also for its superb gardens and nurseries, totalling 480 acres. Created by Alan Bloom in 1973, the railway enthusiast is well catered for with $10^{1}/_{4}$in, 15in and 2ft steam operating lines and a standard gauge museum. The 'Garden Line' opened in 1965, originally $9^{1}/_{4}$in gauge but converted to $10^{1}/_{4}$in during 1995, is the shortest, taking passengers on a ride through the house garden. The 15in gauge 'Waveney Line', opened in 1973 and now $2^{1}/_{2}$ miles in length, runs for part of its journey alongside the River Waveney and is powered by two 1937 Krupp-built German 4-6-2's, *Rosenkavalier* and *Mannertrau* and a 1976-built 4-6-2 *Flying Scotsman*. The 2ft gauge 'Nursery Line', at $2^{1}/_{4}$ miles in length, opened in 1966 and takes passengers through the nurseries which are not normally accessible to the public. Four steam locomotives work this line, including two Hunslet 0-4-0 saddle tanks, *Gwynedd* (built 1883) and *George Sholto* (built 1909), rescued by Alan Bloom from the Penrhyn Slate Quarries in North Wales. Passengers are carried in open toast rack coaches also from the Penrhyn Quarries. The large standard gauge museum houses a total of 10 main line steam locomotives including London, Tilbury & Southend Railway 4-4-2 tank *Thundersley*, LMS 4-6-0 No. 6100 *Royal Scot* and BR Standard 'Britannia' class 4-6-2 No. 70013 *Oliver Cromwell*. The latter engine, on loan from the National Railway Museum (see p.130) hauled the last steam-hauled train on British Railways on August 11 1968.

Bromyard & Linton Light Railway

Broadbridge
Bromyard
Hereford & Worcestershire

Route: Within site
Gauge: 2ft
Open: On Open Days only. See press for details

This narrow gauge line has been built on part of the trackbed at Bromyard on the ex-GWR branch from Worcester to Leominster, opened in 1897 and closed by BR in 1964. During 1995 a platform was built and track laid in the station site. Currently the line is only open to the public on Open Days when demonstration trains will run.

Brookside Miniature Railway

Macclesfield Road
Poynton
Cheshire SK12 1BY

Tel: 01625 872919
Route: Within grounds of garden centre
Length: 1/2 mile
Gauge: 71/4in
Open: Every weekend, Wednesdays April to September, daily July and August
Facilities: Car park, picnic site, railwayana museum

Developed from an original 5in gauge line built in 1972, it was changed to its present gauge in 1989 and a steady acquisition of redundant railway artefacts makes for an interesting display.

Trains depart from a four-platform station complete with turntables, over river bridges and climb steadily through woodland and a 65ft tunnel to the summit of the line. The return journey traverses the same route. Four steam locomotives and four diesels operate trains which are made up from ten sit-astride coaches and four Pullman covered coaches. Future plans include completion of signalling operation from a full size Midland Railway signalbox (originally situated at Southport Aughton Road). The museum of railway artefacts is housed in a re-created GWR waiting room and is situated next to the station.

Bure Valley Railway

Aylsham Station
Norwich Road
Aylsham
Norwich NR11 6BW

Tel: 01263 733858
Route: Aylsham to Wroxham
Length: 9 miles
Gauge: 15in
Open: April to October and December. Telephone for details
Facilities: Car park, shop, refreshments, museum, picnic sites, combined rail/river trips, facilities for disabled

The Bure Valley Railway runs along part of the trackbed of the branch line from Wroxham to Aylsham, opened by the East Norfolk Railway in 1878 and extended to County School in 1880. It was finally closed by BR in 1982. The 15in gauge line cost £21/2 million to build and was opened by author and broadcaster Miles Kington as a miniature passenger-carrying line as recently as 1990. Since then it has had no fewer than five owners. The Bure Valley station at Wroxham is adjacent to that of BR, connected by a footbridge, and has a three-track layout with a turntable. As the line meanders along the valley of the River

Left The well detailed station on the Brookside Miniature Railway *(Brookside Miniature Railway)*

Bure, alongside the Bure Valley Walk, it passes through three other stations, at Coltishall, Brampton and Buxton, before arriving at Aylsham through a ¼-mile long tunnel, where the railway has its overall-roofed terminus, engine sheds and workshops. Four steam and two diesel locomotives operate the line and visiting engines from the Romney Hythe & Dymchurch Railway and the Ravenglass & Eskdale Railway can occasionally be seen at work. Combined rail and Broads boat excursions are available in the summer.

Cadeby Light Railway

The Old Rectory
Cadeby
Nuneaton
Warwickshire CV13 0AS

Tel: 01455 290462
Route: Within Rectory Gardens
Length: 75yd
Gauge: 1ft 11½in
Open: Second Saturday in every month and event days. Telephone for details
Facilities: Refreshments, traction engines, miniature railway, model railway, museum

Situated in the grounds of an old rectory is the late Reverend Teddy Boston's collection which is now managed by his widow and a dedicated team of volunteers. The Cadeby Light Railway first opened in 1963 and locomotives on the line include 1919-built Bagnall 0-4-0 saddle tank *Pixie* and eleven industrial diesel and petrol locomotives together with a Penrhyn Quarryman's coach and various goods wagons. In addition to the narrow gauge railway the rectory is also home to a standard gauge Peckett 0-4-0 saddle tank industrial locomotive, a 5in gauge miniature railway, a large '00' gauge model railway and a museum housing the Boston Collection.

Left 2-6-2 No. 6 waits at Aylsham station with a train for Wroxham on the 15in Bure Valley Railway *(AA Photo Library)*

Chasewater Light Railway & Museum

Brownhills Station
Hednesford Road
Brownhills West
Walsall WS8 7LT

Tel: 01543 452623
Route: Brownhills West to Norton Lakeside
Length: 1¼ miles
Gauge: Standard
Open: Trains run on Sundays from Easter to mid October
Facilities: Car park, shop, refreshments, museum, picnic site

The Chasewater Light Railway is situated on part of the old Midland Railway Brownhills branch line, north of Birmingham, which was opened in 1883 and closed by the LMS in 1930. One of the earliest preservation projects, founded in 1959 as a static museum run by the Railway Preservation Society, it had its first steam day in 1968 and was represented at the Stockton & Darlington Railway 150th anniversary celebrations in 1975. However by 1982 the line had almost closed and it was not until 1988 that it re-opened with a new terminus at Brownhills West. A short extension was opened in 1992 with a further one in December 1995, which takes the railway over the causeway in Chasewater Pleasure Park. Passenger services on the line are handled by a BR diesel multiple unit and the railway is home to a large collection of steam and diesel industrial locomotives. Future plans include an extension to Chasetown, installing a run-round loop at Norton Lakeside and to develop Brownhills West station and yard.

Cheddleton Railway Centre/ Churnet Valley Railway

The Station
Station Road
Cheddleton
Nr Leek
Staffordshire ST13 7EE

Tel: 01538 360522
Route: Within site/Eventually Leekbrook Junction to Oakamoor
Length: 400yd/Eventually 7 miles
Gauge: Standard
Open: April to October and December. Telephone for details
Facilities: Car park, shop, refreshments, museum, picnic site

Situated on the former North Staffordshire Railway line from Rocester to North Rode, opened in 1849 and closed by BR in 1988, the Cheddleton Railway Centre is housed in Cheddleton station building and yard in the picturesque Churnet Valley. Originally opened by a group of preservationists in 1973 who restored the ornate station building, installed a museum and gave steam train rides along the short length of track. In 1994 the Society signed a contract to purchase the seven miles of redundant trackbed between Oakamoor and Leekbrook Junction and launched a share issue in 1995 to raise capital for the re-opening of the line. Tracklaying is progressing rapidly on this picturesque route beside the River Churnet and Caldon Canal. The current schedule for restoring services is to re-open one mile by 1996 and the entire line by 2000. Locomotives based at Cheddleton include former LMS Class 4F 0-6-0 No. 4422 (built 1927), former North Staffordshire Railway 0-6-2 tank No. 2 built in 1923 (on static display), ex-BR Standard 2-6-4 tank No. 80136 built in 1956 (currently under restoration) and several diesels, including ex-BR Class 25 D7672 *Tamworth Castle*.

Cleethorpes Coast Light Railway

Kingsway Station
Kings Road
Cleethorpes
Lincolnshire DN35 0AG

Tel: 01472 604657
Route: Lakeside to Kingsway
Length: 1 mile
Gauge: 15in

Open: Daily Easter to end October, then weekends
Facilities: Car park, shop, refreshments, picnic site

Opened in 1948 as a steam railway this miniature line was subsequently converted to electric operation in 1954 and then to gas hydraulic in 1972. After a change of ownership in 1991 the line was rebuilt and steam returned in 1994. Passenger figures now exceed 65,000 per annum. The railway passes alongside Lakeside Park with fine panoramic views of the Humber Estuary with its excellent beaches, before turning inland through the park area. A major feasibility study has been carried out with the results being approved by the local authority to extend the railway into Cleethorpes Country Park, giving a total run of 2$1/2$ miles. A new museum dedicated to seaside miniature railways is also planned for the future. Rare 15in gauge vintage and veteran steam locomotives are part of one of the largest collections of seaside miniature railway equipment in the country. Steam locomotives operating on the line include 2-4-2s *Katie* and *Sean*, 4-6-2 *Seabreeze*, 4-4-2 *King George*, 4-6-0 *Royal Scot* and 2-8-2 *Konigswinter*.

Colne Valley Railway

Castle Hedingham Station
Yeldham Road
Castle Hedingham
Halstead
Essex CO9 3DZ

Tel: 01787 461174
Route: Either side of Castle Hedingham station
Length: 1 mile
Gauge: Standard
Open: Sundays Easter to October, Tuesdays, Wednesdays and Thursdays of school summer holidays. Many special events. Telephone for details
Facilities: Car park, shop, refreshments, museum, picnic site, Wine & Dine train, educational facilities, facilities for disabled

The Colne Valley & Halstead Railway, completely opened in 1863 between Chappel &

Wakes Colne and Haverhill, survived as an independent company until 1923 when it was absorbed into the LNER. Following a very busy period during World War II the line returned to its normal operation, and after a short experiment with diesel railcars BR ceased passenger services in 1961 and closed the line in 1965. In 1973 a preservation group moved into the site and started to clear the area of ten years of undergrowth. The first 'steam up' was held in 1975 and the first of many educational events was held in 1979. Castle Hedingham station has been re-created on a new site, using the original Colne Valley station building from Castle & Sible Hedingham, and a large quantity of steam and diesel locomotives and rolling stock is now preserved here. The railway specialises in educational visits and is well known for its excellent Pullman dining service. The latter is operated in three historic carriages creating the luxurious atmosphere of an 'Orient Express'-style Pullman dining train. Future plans at Castle Hedingham include building an engine shed, workshop, museums and display area. In the more distant future it is the railway's aim to extend the line to Halstead, making a total distance of 4$1/2$ miles.

Derby Industrial Museum

Silk Mill Lane
Off Full Street
Derby DE1 3AR

Tel: 01332 255308
Open: All day Mondays to Saturdays, Sunday and bank holiday afternoons
Facilities: Car park, shop, facilities for disabled

The museum, opened in 1974, is located on the sites of the world's first modern factories – the silk mills of 1702 and 1717. Displays introduce visitors to Derbyshire's industries, stationary power, railway engineering and research, and aerospace. Of interest to railway enthusiasts are the railway engineering and research gallery with its '0' gauge model railway. A former British Celanese 0-4-0 saddle tank built by Peckett stands guard outside the museum.

East Anglian Railway Museum

Chappel & Wakes Colne Station
Station Road
Wakes Colne
Colchester
Essex CO6 2DS

Tel: 01206 242524
Open: Daily. Telephone for steam operating days
Facilities: Car park, shop, refreshments, museum, miniature railway, heritage centre

This museum contains a comprehensive collection of railway architecture, engineering and relics representing over 100 years of railways in the Eastern Counties. It was formed in 1968 as the Stour Valley Railway Preservation Society to preserve a section of the Stour Valley Railway when closure was threatened. When closure did not take place the museum, a registered charity, was formed in 1986. Chappel & Wakes Colne station is situated on the former GER branch line from Marks Tey to Cambridge via Haverhill. It opened in 1849 and still open today as far as Sudbury. Built in the 1890s the station building is a classic example of GER architecture and is restored to its original condition with a heritage centre situated in the storage arches underneath. Two restored signalboxes include the original one which is no longer in operation, and one that was moved from Mistley, near Manningtree, that now controls train movements within the site. A restored Victorian goods shed is now used for functions. The museum is situated near to Chappel viaduct which was opened in 1849. It is the longest viaduct in East Anglia and is reputed to be the largest brick structure in Europe, containing over seven million bricks, with each of the 32 arches being 30ft wide. A major extension is planned to run over Chappel viaduct, which will extend the running line to approximately one mile. Among the many locomotive exhibits are GER Class N7 0-6-2T No. 69621 built in 1924

Right Preserved signalbox at Chappel & Wakes Colne station, East Anglian Railway Museum (*AA Photo Library*)

and BR Standard Class 4MT 2-6-4T No. 80151 built in 1956. Steam open days are held about 30 times a year with passenger trains and demonstration freight trains.

East Anglia Transport Museum/ East Suffolk Light Railway

Chapel Road
Carlton Colville
Lowestoft
Suffolk NR33 8BL

Tel: 01502 518459
Open: Easter Sunday and Monday, Sundays and bank holidays from May to September, Saturdays June to September, weekdays mid July to end August
Facilities: Car park, shop, refreshments, transport museum, narrow gauge railway, picnic site

A transport museum which includes trams, trolley buses and veteran road vehicles operating in a 1930s street scene. The 2ft gauge railway, known as the East Suffolk Railway, carries passengers along a 300yd line between Chapel Road and Woodside within the site of the museum. Opened in 1973 and based on light railway operation with track from a former sand quarry, Canvey Island and the long-closed Southwold Railway (see p.110), the line is fully signalled with a GER signalbox from the Lowestoft area. The railway's two industrial diesel locomotives date from the 1930s.

Echills Wood Railway

National Agricultural Centre
Stoneleigh Park
Warwickshire CV8 2LZ

Tel: 01926 53244
Route: Within grounds of National Agricultural Centre
Length: $1/2$ mile
Gauge: $7^1/4$in
Open: 26-30 days, at major Shows, and by private arrangement. Telephone for details

Facilities: Train rides only. Other facilities available within main site

The Echills Wood Railway is one of the permanent attractions of the National Agricultural Centre, home of the Royal Show. It was established in 1975 at the invitation of the NAC and is owned and operated by a group of local enthusiasts. The railway consists of a staggered platform terminus, 'Harvesters', from which a single line leads to Echills Wood where there is a circuit which doubles as a return loop. The line operates a comprehensive electro-mechanical signalling system, correctly interlocked, with a single-line token for the section between 'Harvesters' and Echills Wood. The railway's own passenger stock consists of purpose-built bogie vehicles equipped with automatic vacuum brake. Locomotives are the property of the members and are mainly narrow gauge steam prototypes.

Ferry Meadows Miniature Railway

Nene Valley Park
Peterborough
Cambs

Tel: 01205 364352
Route: Within Nene Valley Park
Length: $1/4$ mile
Gauge: $10^1/4$in
Open: Easter school holidays, weekends May to September and daily during school summer holidays
Facilities: Car park, refreshments

An out-and-back miniature railway, opened in 1978, operates from a station adjacent to the cafe, to the children's play area within the Nene Valley Park. Motive power is provided by two steam locomotives and one diesel locomotive. The older of the two steam locomotives is a freelance 4-6-2 which was originally built for the boxer, Randolph Turpin, for use on his private railway. Future plans include extending the length of the line.

Foxfield Steam Railway

Caverswall Road Station
Blythe Bridge
Stoke-on-Trent
Staffs

Tel: 01782 396210 (weekends)/01270 874959 (weekdays)
Route: Blythe Bridge to Dilhorne Park
Length: $2^1/2$ miles
Gauge: Standard
Open: Sundays and bank holiday Mondays Easter to September
Facilities: Car park, shop, refreshments, museum, facilities for disabled

Operating on an old colliery line, opened in 1893 and closed in 1965, the Foxfield Railway is situated very close to Blythe Bridge station on the main Stoke-on-Trent to Derby railway line. After closure a preservation group took over and passengers were first carried in 1967, with Caverswall Station being opened in 1982. Small and powerful industrial steam and diesel locomotives haul trains up fearsome gradients to a summit 705ft above sea level. The large collection of locomotives includes 15 steam, 12 diesel and two battery electric engines. Future plans include opening both ends of the railway to passenger operation, including the 1-in-19 Dilhorne Bank, and developing a mining museum at the old colliery.

Great Central Railway

Loughborough Central Station
Great Central Road
Loughborough
Leicestershire LE11 1RW

Tel: 01509 230726
Route: Loughborough Central to Leicester North
Length: 8 miles
Gauge: Standard

Right Industrial 0-6-0 saddle tanks on the Foxfield Light Railway (AA Photo Library)

Open: Weekends and bank holiday Mondays all year, daily May to October
Facilities: Car park, shop, refreshments, museum, picnic sites, Wine & Dine trains, steam driving courses, facilities for disabled

Britain's last main line, the Great Central Railway, was opened in 1899 and linked Manchester, Sheffield and Nottingham with Marylebone station in London. Designed for fast traffic with a continental loading gauge and no level crossings, the railway was never a great success and was eventually closed by BR in 1969. The section from Loughborough to Quorn & Woodhouse was re-opened by the Main Line Steam Trust in 1973, to Rothley in 1976 and finally to Leicester North in 1991. The northern part of the line between Loughborough and Rothley is being doubled, with even a section of quadruple track, so that the railway can operate with the appearance of a main line. The 2³/₄-mile double track section between Rothley and Quorn is already laid, with the section between Quorn and Loughborough due to be completed by 1999, to coincide with the centenary of the original Great Central. A future 10-mile extension northwards is planned, to Ruddington on the outskirts of Nottingham (see next entry). A very large collection of impressive main line preserved steam and diesel locomotives is based on the GCR to provide a variety of train operations, and visiting engines can frequently be seen in action. Stations have been restored to different periods in the railway's history – Loughborough is typical of the 1960s, Quorn & Woodhouse recreates the 1940s, Rothley captures the Edwardian era and Leicester North is currently being developed into a three-platform main line terminus. Passengers are conveyed in traditional main line style through delightful Leicestershire hunting countryside and, en route, cross Swithland Reservoir on two viaducts totalling ¹/₂-mile in length. On certain days Wine & Dine trains are operated, serving six-course meals.

Left LNER Class A4 4-6-2 No. 60007 *Sir Nigel Gresley* on the Great Central Railway, November 8 1994 *(Mike Esau)*

Hudswell-Clarke 0-6-0ST in action at the Nottingham Heritage Centre *(Nottingham Heritage Centre)*

Great Central Railway (Nottingham)

Nottingham Heritage Centre
Mere Way
Ruddington
Nottingham NG11 6NX

Tel: 0115 9405705
Route: Within country park
Length: 1 mile
Gauge: Standard
Open: Sundays and bank holidays Easter to late October
Facilities: Car park, shop, museum, refreshments, picnic site, miniature railway

The railway is situated at the 11¹/₂-acre Nottingham Heritage Centre within the Rushcliffe Country Park on part of the site of a former Ministry of Defence ordnance depot. Within the heritage centre is a bus collection and a museum, and former MOD buildings house the locomotives. The mile-long railway has been rebuilt on the original trackbed of the military railway as far as its former junction with the Great Central main line. Locomotives in use are ex-Corby Steel Works 0-6-0 saddle tank No. 56 and ex-Castle Donington Power Station 0-4-0 saddle tank No. 2. Three former BR diesels are under restoration. Work is under way refurbishing three miles of the former GCR main line as far as Rushcliffe Halt, and opening is planned for Easter 1997. In addition to the standard gauge railway an 800yd-long triple-gauge miniature railway is almost completed on the site.

Great Eastern Railway Company

County School Station
North Elmham
East Dereham
Norfolk NR20 5LE

Tel: 01362 668181
Route: Within site at County School station

Length: 3/4 mile
Gauge: Standard
Open: Daily Easter to end October, trains operate most weekends
Facilities: Car park, museum, refreshments, facilities for disabled

County School station is situated on the former Great Eastern Railway line from Wymondham to Wells-next-the-Sea, which opened in 1849 and was closed to passengers by BR in 1964. The section from Wymondham to North Elmham was finally closed to all traffic in 1989. Operations are currently limited to train rides within the site, but future plans for re-opening the line are not only dependent on the outcome of discussions with the British Rail Property Board but also on the nearby Mid Norfolk Railway Society's scheme (see p.101). Operating steam locomotives include Andrew Barclay 0-4-0 saddle tank *Edmunsons* and 0-4-0 saddle tank *Pony*. On static display is an 0-6-0 pannier tank. Diesel motive power consists of a Ruston Hornsby and a 3-car DMU.

Great Northern & East Lincolnshire Railway

Ludborough Station
Station Road
Ludborough
Lincs

Open: Most weekends
Facilities: Car park, museum

A short standard gauge railway which is based at the restored Ludborough station on the former Great Northern Railway's route between Grimsby Town and Louth, opened in 1848 and closed by BR in 1964. A limited quantity of goods wagons, one diesel shunter and two non-working steam locomotives are housed at the site. A collection of Lincolnshire railway artefacts and model railway are housed in a small museum on the site.

Halton Miniature Railway

Town Park
Stockham Lane
Palacefields
Runcorn
Cheshire

Tel: 01928 574396
Route: Within Town Park, Runcorn
Length: 1 mile
Gauge: 7¼in
Open: Sundays and bank holiday Monday afternoons all year

This miniature railway opened in 1979 and has been gradually extended to its current extensive layout within the Town Park. The railway owns three locomotives, all petrol hydraulic – a 2-8-0 American-style steam outline, a 'Hymek'-style Bo-Bo and a 0-4-0 Hunslet type. Two major steam events are held each year, in April and September.

Hilcote Valley Railway

Fletchers Garden Centre
Stone Road
Eccleshall
Nr Stafford
Staffs ST21 6JY

Tel: 01785 284553
Route: Through garden centre and around lake
Length: 3/4 mile
Gauge: 7¼in
Open: Weekends March to October, bank holidays and daily in August
Facilities: Car park, shop, refreshments, special railway weekends (telephone for details)

This miniature railway was designed and built in 1993 by Roger Greatrex and includes prototype equipment such as signalbox, ticket office, raised platform, turntable, tunnel, girder bridge and signal gantry. The line runs around the garden centre, then into the country at the rear, around a lake and over a bridge before returning through a tunnel back into the centre. The bridge is a replica of one built by the Earl of Dudley's ironworks in 1907 for J A Holder's miniature railway at Broome Hall, near Stourbridge. Trains are hauled by either an 0-6-0 Bagnall diesel, an 0-6-0 Kerr Stuart 'Haig' class tender locomotive *Kashmir* and Bo-Bo GP40 Union Pacific diesel.

Irchester Narrow Gauge Railway Museum

Irchester Country Park
Wellingborough
Northants

Open: Every Sunday and bank holiday Mondays

A collection, put together since 1972, of industrial steam and diesel narrow gauge locomotives and rolling stock connected with the ironstone industries of Northamptonshire and the East Midlands. Operating weekends are held in the last full weekend of each month from March to October.

Ironbridge Gorge Museum

Ironbridge
Telford
Shropshire TF8 7AW

Tel: 01952 433522(weekdays)/
01952 432166(weekends)
Open: Daily during summer. Telephone for details of winter openings
Facilities: Car parks, shop, refreshments

A large open air museum, spread over six square miles, devoted to the Industrial Revolution and based near the famous Iron Bridge near Coalbrookdale. The main site is at Blists Hill where exhibits include furnace blowing machines and the Hay inclined plane of the Shropshire Union Canal. Of interest to railway historians is the working replica of Trevithick's first steam railway locomotive, which was built by apprentices of GKN Sankey in Telford. The original locomotive ran on the Coalbrookdale company's 3ft gauge plateway tracks. The replica weighs 4$\frac{1}{2}$ tons with a top speed of 5mph and runs on a 100ft diameter track.

Kidderminster Railway Museum

Station Drive
Comberton Hill
Kidderminster
Worcs DY10 1QX

Tel: 01562 825316
Open: When Severn Valley Railway is operating (see p.109)
Facilities: Shop, refreshments, ground floor facilities for disabled

A large collection of railway ephemera and artefacts, from all over Britain, is housed in the beautifully restored former Great Western Railway warehouse adjacent to the Severn Valley Railway station at Kidderminster. Included in the displays are several hands-on signalling and telecommunication displays.

Leasowes Park Miniature Railway

Leasowes Park
Mucklow Hill
Halesowen
West Midlands

Tel: 01562 710614
Route: Within Leasowes Park
Length: 450yd
Gauge: 7$\frac{1}{4}$in
Open: Sunday afternoons
Facilities: Car park

This miniature railway has been operating since 1990 along the towpath of Dudley No. 2 Canal on the Birmingham Canal Navigations. The route starts in the car park and after passing through woodland arrives at the park lake. Motive power consists of 2-6-2 steam locomotive *Prince Edward* built in 1932, and petrol-engined diesel-outline *William Shenstone* built in 1990.

Above 2-6-2 *Prince Edward* on the 7$\frac{1}{4}$in gauge Leasowes Park Miniature Railway (*Leasowes Park Miniature Railway*)

Legbourne Railway Museum

The Old Station
Legbourne
Louth
Lincolnshire LN11 8LH

Tel: 01507 603116
Open: bank holiday Mondays and Tuesdays to Sundays Easter to end September
Facilities: Car park, shop, picnic site, facilities for disabled

This railway museum is centred on Britain's oldest preserved Great Northern Railway station building. The purpose-built museum houses over 2000 railway relics mainly of Lincolnshire origin. A restored and fully equipped GNR signalbox, originally from Sutton-on-Sea, is also open to the public.

Mangapps Farm Railway Museum

Southminster Road
Burnham-on-Crouch
Essex CM0 8QQ

Tel: 01621 784898
Open: Weekend afternoons and bank holidays all year (except Christmas) and daily during school holidays
Facilities: Car park, shop, refreshments, museum, picnic site

A railway centre which features the railway history of East Anglia and which opened on a greenfield site in 1989. A variety of steam and diesel locomotives, rolling stock and signalling is on display in addition to an exhibition hall of railway artefacts. Restored station buildings from the Great Eastern Railway, Mid-Suffolk Light Railway and the Midland & Great Northern Joint Railway are also on display. A $\frac{1}{2}$-mile length of

track (soon to be extended) gives passenger rides behind some of the centre's steam and diesel locomotives, including 1954-built Bagnall 0-6-0 saddle tank *Demelza*.

Midland Railway Centre

Butterley Station
Nr Ripley
Derbyshire DE5 3QZ

Tel: 01773 747674/01773 570140
Route: Hammersmith to Ironville
Length: 3½ miles
Gauge: Standard, 2ft, 5in, 3½in
Open: Every weekend March to October and December. Every Wednesday April to October. Daily August and most school holidays
Facilities: Car park, shop, refreshments, museum, picnic site, narrow gauge and miniature railways, Wine & Dine trains, 35-acre country park, facilities for disabled

The Midland Railway Centre is situated on part of the former Midland Railway line from Pye Bridge to Ambergate, opened in 1875 and closed by BR in 1968. Re-opened by a preservation group in 1973, the first passenger trains ran in 1981. With its headquarters at Butterley, the Centre famous for its quality restoration work, occupies a 57-acre site and operates trains along a 3½-mile section of track including a viaduct over Butterley reservoir. Over 45 steam locomotives, including LMS 4-6-2s *Princess Elizabeth*, *Princess Margaret Rose* and *Duchess of Sutherland* (recently purchased from Bressingham Steam Museum), main line diesels (including examples from Classes 03, 08, 20, 25, 31, 37, 40, 44, 45, 46, 47 and 55) and a very large collection of rolling stock are based at the Centre, which also features the Golden Valley Light Railway working narrow gauge line and two miniature railways. The Matthew Kirtley Museum, in its large trainshed, contains a varied display of historic steam, diesel and electric locomotives. The

Left SDJR 2-8-0 No. 53809 and LMS 0-6-0T No. 47357 at the Midland Railway Centre, Butterley, August 25 1991 *(Robin Stewart-Smith)*

standard gauge operating line is authentically signalled and boasts three fully restored Midland Railway signalboxes, originally from Kettering, Ais Gill and Kilby Bridge. Future plans include the building of a railway village, diesel depot, Historical Model Railway Society headquarters, road transport gallery, new locomotive depot, extending the narrow gauge line into the Country Park, building 21in and 9½in gauge lines and re-opening the standard gauge colliery branch line from Swanwick Junction. An extension to Pye Bridge, with an interchange station on the main Sheffield to Nottingham line, is also proposed.

Mid Norfolk Railway Preservation Trust

Yaxham Station
Dereham
Norfolk

This new preservation group has recently been formed by former members of the Great Eastern Railway project at County School station (see p.97). The aim is to re-open the former Great

Eastern Railway 17-mile branch line, opened in 1849 and closed to passengers in 1964, from Wymondham to Wells-next-the-Sea on the BR Cambridge to Norwich line. The section from Wymondham to North Elmham did not finally close until 1989.

Mid-Suffolk Light Railway

Brockford Station
Wetheringsett
Nr Stowmarket
Suffolk IP14 5PW

Tel: 01473 742358
Open: Sundays and bank holidays Easter to September. Wednesdays in school summer holidays
Facilities: Car park, shop, refreshments, railway walk, picnic site

Below Brockford station on the Mid-Suffolk Light Railway *(John Broadribb)*

The Mid-Suffolk Light Railway was an ambitious scheme to build lines from Haughley to Halesworth via Stradbroke and Laxfield, with a branch from Kenton to Westerfield. Work started in 1902, and the line was completed for 21 miles as far as Cratfield by 1904, when goods traffic started. Severe financial difficulties prevented much work on the Kenton to Westerfield line, although it was partly constructed as far as Debenham. The line went into receivership before the opening to passengers in 1908 between Haughley and Laxfield. There were difficulties crossing the marshes near Halesworth, and before long the line beyond Laxfield, and all of the Westerfield branch were abandoned. The company remained independent of the Great Eastern Railway, and was taken over by the LNER in 1924. It survived the latter's proposal to turn it into a motor road in the 1930s, and closed to all traffic in 1952, being lifted the following year. The present museum was established in 1991, and has brought a number of original MSLR buildings from Mendlesham, Brockford and Wolby on to the site. The intention is to portray the station as it was in its heyday, and ultimately to offer visitors a ride in a restored train of the period. The society also intends to collect artefacts and other memorabilia, as well as personal reminiscences from those who knew or worked on the line. Visitors can use the Trackbed Walk of about one mile and also the waymarked Middy Light Railway Long Distance Path between Haughley and Brockford. The Society has a lease on 1,200yd of trackbed and is working to extend its track along this length. A Hudswell-Clarke 0-6-0 saddle tank, No. 1604, built in 1928, is currently on static display. Several ex-GER carriages and goods wagons are being restored.

Below Working trams at the National Tramway Museum, Crich *(National Tramway Museum)*

Moseley Railway Museum

c/o Ridge Danyers College
Northdowns Road
Cheadle
Stockport
Cheshire SK8 5HA

Tel: 0161 4852588
Open: Second Sunday each month or by appointment
Facilities: Car park, refreshments, model toys, train rides, facilities for disabled

Originally founded as a school project when the gauge was 1ft 8in, but this had been converted to 2ft by 1978. The museum houses a large collection of industrial narrow gauge railway equipment, including 40 internal combustion locomotives and nearly 100 pieces of rolling stock. The majority of the locomotives, most in running order, are either diesel or petrol and include unusual examples dating back to the 1920s and rare World War I examples. They include the products of most major British manufacturers, including Ruston & Hornsby, Motor Rail and Hunslet. The large rolling stock collection of industrial wagons includes 'V' skips, bomb wagons, peat wagons and mine wagons. The Society's aim is to be a working museum and rides are given on a 1/2-mile 2ft gauge track which skirts fields in the college grounds. Track is being presently upgraded in preparation for the arrival of a steam locomotive. Future plans include extending the line into nearby Bruntwood Park and building new workshops.

National Tramway Museum

Crich
Nr Matlock
Derbyshire DE4 5DP

Tel: 01773 852565
Open: Daily April to October except some Fridays. Sundays in March and November
Facilities: Car park, refreshments, shop, picnic sites, exhibition hall, facilities for disabled

The museum houses Europe's largest collection of trams with over 70 examples of vintage electric, steam and horse-drawn examples, a third of which are regularly in passenger-carrying service. Included are examples from the UK, Prague, Portugal, South Africa and New York. The Tramway Museum Society was formed in 1955, and in 1959 acquired the site at Crich, a former mineral railway built by George Stephenson in 1842. 1963 saw the first horse-drawn public service, and 1964 was the first day of electric public service. A journey along the tramway takes passengers from Townend through the Museum's period street, under the Bowes-Lyon bridge and into open countryside to the Glory Mine Terminus, with views over the Derwent Valley.

Nene Valley Railway

Wansford Station
Stibbington
Peterborough
Cambs PE8 6LR

Tel: 01780 782854/01780 782921 (talking timetable)
Route: Yarwell Junction to Peterborough (NVR)
Length: 7¹/₂ miles
Gauge: Standard (continental loading gauge)
Open: Weekends Easter to end October, weekdays May to end August. Santa Specials in December. Telephone for details
Facilities: Car park, shop, refreshments, museum, facilities for disabled

Originally part of the London & North Western Railway's route from Peterborough to Blisworth, opened in 1845 and closed by BR in 1966, the Nene Valley Railway is now well known for its international flavour and location filming for TV and cinema. Since 1974, with assistance from Peterborough Development Corporation, the Peterborough Railway Society has had its

Right LNER Class A3 4-6-2 No. 60103 *Flying Scotsman* disguised as No. 60106 *Flying Fox*, Nene Valley Railway, May 6 1994 *(Mike Esau)*

headquarters at Wansford, which has become the main centre for foreign locomotives and rolling stock in Britain. Trains started operating in 1977 and a new NVR station at Peterborough (Nene Valley) was opened in 1986 adjacent to a site which is being developed into an international railway museum. From Peterborough the line runs through Nene Park along the banks of the River Nene, crossing the river twice, and into open countryside, before passing through Wansford and the 616yd Wansford Tunnel. Current restored stock on the NVR consists of examples from Germany, Denmark, Sweden, France, and Belgium as well as many from Britain, including the line's first locomotive, former BR Class 5MT 4-6-0 No. 73050 *City of Peterborough*. Film makers have taken advantage of the continental flavour and the NVR stations are often cleverly disguised as foreign locations for films such as *Octopussy* and *Goldeneye*, television dramas and commercials. A new station building will be opened in 1996 and developments in the future will concentrate on restoration of present stock.

Peckett 0-4-0ST No. 2104 shunts Pitsford Sidings on the Northampton & Lamport Railway, December 4 1994 *(J B Pepper)*

Northampton & Lamport Railway

Pitsford & Brampton Station
Pitsford Road
Chapel Brampton
Northampton NN6 8BA

Tel: 01604 820327 (mainly Sundays)
Route: Within station site
Length: 3/4 mile
Gauge: Standard
Open: Site open Sundays. Passenger operations Sundays and bank holidays Easter to end October
Facilities: Car park, shop, refreshments

The Northampton to Market Harborough branch was opened by the London & North Western Railway in 1859 and included six stations and two tunnels. It was first closed to passengers in April 1960 but re-opened to through traffic in January 1961, closed again in May 1961 and then re-opened a second time in July 1972. The passenger service was finally withdrawn in August 1973 and

the line completely closed in August 1981. The Society originally started around the same time as the line closure, moved once and changed its name twice before finally becoming the Northampton & Lamport Railway. The railway presently extends for 3/4-mile with Pitsford & Brampton station roughly at the centre. The route shares the original track formation with the Brampton Valley Walk, a linear park operated by Northamptonshire County Council. The signalbox at Pitsford Ironstone exchange sidings is an example of a rare 10ft-square LNWR type which was originally located at Wolverton works. Another LNWR signalbox, originally from Little Bowden level crossing, controls the station site. The first public steam train operated in 1995 and a Light Railway Order has been granted northwards to Spratton, which will allow the railway to extend to approximately three miles in length. In the more distant future it is hoped to extend to Lamport, giving a total run of seven miles. A good collection of both steam and diesel main line and industrial locomotives is based at the site.

Northamptonshire Ironstone Railway Trust

Hunsbury Hill Railway Museum
Hunsbury Hill Road
West Hunsbury
Northampton

Tel: 01604 890229
Route: Museum Halt to Tunnel Halt
Length: 1 3/4 miles
Gauge: Standard
Open: Sundays and bank holidays all year. Trains operate Sunday afternoons April to September
Facilities: Car park, shop, refreshments, picnic site

The ironworks at Hunsbury were built in 1873, and to transport the iron ore from the quarries to the ironworks a horse-drawn gravity tramway was constructed in 1875. It was built to a gauge of 3ft 8in and was one of the earliest ironstone tramways. Locomotive power was introduced in

1912 when the gravity system was replaced. The ironworks closed in 1921 and the tramway was dismantled in the late 1930s. The Northamptonshire Ironstone Trust was formed in 1974 and the present standard gauge railway runs along part of the original tramway trackbed. Passenger services started in 1982 over a loop section and in 1983 over the complete section. The main engine shed and museum building were erected in 1984 and house the museum display, workshop and locomotive repair facilities. A fine collection of Aveling Porter and Sentinel steam locomotives, along with some former industrial diesels give brakevan rides on operating days.

North Ings Farm Museum Railway

Dorrington
Lincolnshire LN4 3QB

Tel: 01526 833100
Route: Within museum site
Length: 440yd
Gauge: 2ft
Open: Saturday afternoons and Sundays Easter to end October
Facilities: Car park, refreshments

A small museum which opened to the public in 1990 and contains a selection of agricultural machinery and other items of interest. A 2ft narrow gauge railway started life in 1972 when the farm was being used for poultry. During the very wet winter of 1971/72 the dumper trucks which were used to serve the 19 sheds became bogged down, and as a result the first items of railway equipment were purchased. The railway was an immediate success and several other items were purchased. In 1981 the poultry business closed, and the railway took on a new role conveying materials around the site. In 1988 the track to the lower lake was opened and since then the railway has proved a major attraction for visitors to the farm. Seven diesels and a 0-4-0 vertical boiler steam locomotive are based on the railway, and passengers are carried in four coaches built on skip chassis. Future plans include new locomotive and carriage sheds.

Above Aveling & Porter 0-4-0GT No. 8800 *Sir Vincent*, built in 1917, at Hunsbury Hill, Northamptonshire Ironstone Trust, March 4 1993 *(Northamptonshire Ironstone Trust)*

Right Hudson Hunslet 0-4-0 diesel hauls a very basic passenger train on the North Ings Farm Museum Railway *(North Ings Farm Museum Railway)*

North Norfolk Railway

Sheringham Station
Sheringham
Norfolk NR26 8RA

Tel: 01263 822045/01263 825449 (talking
timetable)
Route: Sheringham to Holt
Length: 5^1/$_4$ miles
Gauge: Standard
Open: March to October. Telephone for details
Facilities: Car park, shop, refreshments, museum,
Wine & Dine train, facilities for disabled

The steeply-graded North Norfolk Railway route
was originally part of the meandering Midland &
Great Northern Joint Railway which linked the
Midlands and Peterborough with Cromer, Great
Yarmouth and Norwich. The majority of this
fascinating cross-country line was closed in 1959.
The present NNR is on the trackbed of the Melton
Constable to Cromer Beach branch of the
MGNJR, which was closed by BR in 1964. After
several rather optimistic preservation plans on
other parts of the system were rejected as being
impractical, the preservation group moved in,
initially at Weybourne, and has now made its
headquarters at Sheringham. In 1969, the year
John Betjeman became the NNR's president, the
railway became the first of the preservation
societies to be floated as a Public Company, and
by 1989 the present route had been fully re-opened.
The restored period stations, particularly at
Weybourne, have often been used as TV and film
locations. A journey along the line provides
passengers with views of the Norfolk coastline
and heathland, and a large collection of restored
steam and diesel locomotives and ex-LNER rolling
stock operate the trains. The current star of the
railway is ex-LNER Class B12 4-6-0 No. 8572,
built in 1928, and was returned to traffic in early
1995 after a major three and a half year rebuild at
Mansfeld locomotive works in Germany. Other

Left Barclay 0-6-0T *Harlaxton* heads a train
between Weybourne and Holt on the North
Norfolk Railway *(Sean Taylor)*

steam locomotives include Great Eastern Railway
Class J15 0-6-0 No. 564, built in 1912, and
several industrial examples built by Hunslet,
Andrew Barclay and Bagnall. A railway museum
and museum signalbox are open to the public at
Sheringham.

Oswestry Bicycle & Railway Museum

Oswald Road
Oswestry
Shropshire SY11 1RE

Tel: 01691 671749
Open: Daily
Facilities: Car park, shop

This new combined railway and bicycle museum
opened in 1991. The railway museum is operated
by the Cambrian Railways Society, who
eventually hope to run a steam train service from
Gobowen to Llanyblodwell through unspoilt
Borderland scenery. The museum and depot were
part of a major railway complex in Oswestry that,
until grouping in 1922, was the headquarters of
the Cambrian Railways. As late as the 1960s,
Oswestry was the headquarters for the Central
Wales Division of BR Western Region and the
workshops were one of the last locations to
undertake steam locomotive repairs. On display
in the old railway building are artefacts from the
Cambrian Railways with some arranged in a
former GWR autocar. Three steam locomotives
are currently operational and can be seen working
on operating days on the ^{1}/$_4$-mile length of track
within the site. They are a Beyer Peacock Works
engine built in 1887, a 1951 Peckett and a 1952
Hunslet. Other steam and diesel locomotives are
awaiting restoration.

Papplewick Miniature Railway

Papplewick Pumping Station
Longdale Lane
Ravenshead
Nr Mansfield
Notts

Tel: 0115 9632938
Route: Within site of Pumping Station museum
Length: 330yd
Gauge: 7^1/$_4$in
Open: On museum open days. Telephone for
details
Facilities: Car park

The former Victorian pumping station, including
two James Watt beam engines, has been
beautifully restored to working order. Among the
many working exhibits is the steam-operated
passenger-carrying miniature railway in the
grounds of the museum.

Peak Rail

Matlock Station
Matlock
Derbyshire DE4 3NA

Tel: 01629 580381
Route: Matlock (BR connection) to Rowsley
Length: 3^1/$_2$ miles
Gauge: Standard
Open: Weekends April to October. Some
weekdays during summer. Telephone for details
Facilities: Car park, shop, refreshments, facilities
for disabled

The former Midland Railway main line from
London St Pancras to Manchester Central was
originally opened in 1849 and closed by BR
between Matlock and Blackwell Mill (near
Buxton) in 1968. It was 1975 before a
preservation society took over the trackbed of this
picturesque line through the heart of the Peak
District National Park. Initially work was
commenced at both Buxton and Matlock but this
was later confined to the latter end, where the
railway makes an end-on connection with the
national system. Passenger trains started running
again to Darley Dale in 1991, with an extension
to Rowsley opening in 1996. Further extensions
are planned to complete eventually what will be a
magnificent 20-mile long scenic railway. A large
collection of steam and diesel locomotives is
based on the line.

Pentney Park Railway

Pentney Park Caravan Site
Pentney
Kings Lynn
Norfolk PE32 1HU

Tel: 01760 337479
Route: Within caravan site
Length: ³/₄ mile
Gauge: 7¹/₄in
Open: Saturdays 5-7pm and Sunday afternoons
June to August and bank holidays

This miniature line was started in 1986 and the 4,000ft of track gives an out-and-back ride with a return loop and passing loops. It runs around the perimeter of the caravan park through woodland and open country with a variety of gradients. Trains are operated by a Class 47 diesel outline locomotive powered by a Briggs & Stratton engine.

Pleasurewood Hills Theme Park

Corton Road
Lowestoft
Suffolk

Tel: 01502 513627
Route: Within theme park
Length: ¹/₂ mile, each route
Gauge: 7¹/₄in and 2ft
Open: Easter to end October
Facilities: Normal theme park facilities

Two separate railways, one narrow gauge and the other a miniature line, are one of the many attractions of this theme park. The route, including tunnels, takes passengers through woodland and at one point the two lines cross each other. Basic stations are provided on each line and passenger journeys are part of the overall entrance fee to the park. Motive power consists of a diesel locomotive on the 7¹/₄in line, and a petrol engine on the 2ft line.

Railway Age

Crewe Heritage Centre
Vernon Way
Crewe
Cheshire CW1 2DB

Tel: 01270 212130
Open: Daily mid February to mid December
Facilities: Car park, shop, refreshments, picnic site, weekend train rides, miniature railway, facilities for disabled

A standard gauge railway restoration centre, opened in 1987, adjacent to the West Coast Main Line near Crewe station houses a changing collection of mainly ex-BR main line diesel and electric locomotives. Of special interest are London & North Western 2-2-2 *Cornwall*, built in 1847, and the unique Brown-Boveri gas turbine No. 18000. Preserved examples of ex-BR diesels include Classes 03, 08, 15, 20, 25, 37, 45, 46, 47, 50 and 52. Passenger rides are given at weekends in steam-hauled brakevans over the 300yd of track within the site. Steam locomotives are stabled here when working special trains to the North Wales coast. In addition there are three working signalboxes, a tea room in the remains of the cancelled Advanced Passenger Train, a collection of railway artefacts and a ¹/₂-mile long passenger-carrying 7¹/₄in gauge miniature railway.

Rudyard Lake Railway

Rudyard Old Station
Rudyard
Nr Leek
Staffs ST13 8PF

Tel: 01260 272862
Route: Rudyard to Hunthouse Wood
Length: 1¹/₂ miles
Gauge: 10¹/₄in
Open: Weekends March to end October and weekday afternoons during school holidays
Facilities: Car park, picnic site

This miniature railway conveys passengers along a very scenic part of the old North Staffordshire Railway Churnet Valley line beside Rudyard Lake, opened in 1849 and closed by BR in 1962. The southern terminus and headquarters are situated at the site of the old NSR Rudyard station and consists of a single platform, run-round loop and four-road locomotive shed with turntable. The northern terminus is at Hunthouse Wood, one mile to the south of the former NSR Rudyard Lake station, and also has a single platform, run-round loop and a small wooden locomotive shed with turntable. Construction began in 1984 and limited services started in 1985: the present route was opened throughout in 1992. Trains are operated by two diesel mechanicals, one petrol mechanical and two steam locomotives, of which the most recent is 2-6-2 tank No. 6 *River Churnet*, built in 1993.

Rushden Historical Transport Museum

The Railway Station
Station Approach
Rushden
Northants

Tel: 01933 318988
Open: Sundays
Facilities: Car park, museum, refreshments

Rushden station, now a transport museum, was situated on the former Midland Railway branch line from Wellingborough to Higham Ferrers, opened in 1893 and closed completely in 1969. Included in its collection are many railway artefacts, an Andrew Barclay 0-4-0 steam locomotive and signalling equipment. The former waiting rooms have been converted to a social club with a Victorian-style real ale bar complete with gas lighting. Future plans include re-opening a one mile length of track to Higham Ferrers.

Right Rutland Railway Museum's 0-4-0ST *Singapore*, built by Hawthorn Leslie in 1936, in steam at Duxford *(Rutland Railway Museum)*

Rutland Railway Museum

Cottesmore Iron Ore Mines Siding
Ashwell Road
Cottesmore
Leics LE15 7BX

Tel: 01572 813203
Open: Most weekends. Telephone for steaming days
Facilities: Car park, shop, refreshments, picnic sites, museum, train rides

The ironstone quarries around the village of Cottesmore were opened during 1882 and the Midland Railway constructed a branch line to connect with the quarry system. A 3ft gauge railway was laid in the quarries to bring tubs of ore down to the standard gauge line via a rope incline. Extensive sidings were put in as quarries were developed at nearby Burley and Exton, served by standard gauge lines. The narrow gauge system was replaced by Euclid dumper lorries in 1957 and the Cottesmore quarries closed in 1965. Closure of the other quarries followed in 1973 and the whole of the track was lifted. A group of railway enthusiasts moved to Cottesmore in 1979 to set up an open air museum. The Museum's collection of industrial steam and diesel locomotives has grown considerably over the years together with a selection of wagons with which to demonstrate the workings of railway in industry. The collection includes 36 mainly industrial steam and diesel locomotives and 60 wagons, vans and coaches. Other relevant artefacts, such as Euclid dumper lorries, and visitor facilities have been added as the Museum continues to develop. Free train rides in brakevans, and demonstration freight trains operate along a ¾-mile length of track within the site. There is an admission charge to the site during working weekends.

Severn Valley Railway

Railway Station
Bewdley
Worcs DY12 1BG

Tel: 01299 403816/01299 401001 (talking timetable)
Route: Bridgnorth to Kidderminster
Length: 16 miles
Gauge: Standard
Open: Every weekend throughout the year, daily mid May to end September
Facilities: Car parks, shop, refreshments, model railway, picnic site, restaurant car, facilities for disabled

One of Britain's premier preserved lines, the Severn Valley Railway is situated on the former GWR branch from Hartlebury to Shrewsbury, opened in 1862 and closed to passengers by BR in 1963. The initial preservation group started fund-raising in 1965, and the first public train ran in 1970 from Bridgnorth to Hampton Loade. The service was extended to Bewdley in 1974 and to Kidderminster in 1984. Since then the line has become a huge success with its large collection of steam and diesel locomotives and rolling stock. Much restoration work is carried out by the railway's workshops which are famed for their high standards of work. The country stations on the line have all been carefully restored to their former GWR glory and a journey along the scenic route which mostly follows the River Severn, evokes all the atmosphere of the heyday of train travel. The major engineering structure on the line is the graceful cast-iron Victoria Bridge, built in 1861, which carries trains on its 200ft span, high above the River Severn. Several enthusiasts weekends are held every year, when visiting locomotives from other preserved railways can be seen in action. Good connections with the main line network at Kidderminster, with its newly-constructed brick-built terminus, and a frequent steam-operated service have ensured the railway's continuing success. A total of 29 locomotives are based on the SVR and on a peak service day five steam locomotives are required for the trains. Steam locomotives include LNER Class K4 2-6-0 No. 3442 *The Great Marquess*, ex-WD 2-10-0 No. 600 *Gordon*, LMS 'Jubilee' class 4-6-0 No. 5690 *Leander*, GWR 'Modified Hall' class 4-6-0 No. 6960 *Raveningham Hall*, GWR 'Hall' class 4-6-0 No. 4930 *Hagley Hall* and 'Manor' class 4-6-0 No. 7802 *Bradley Manor*. Former BR diesels include examples of Classes 08, 11, 25, 27, 50 and 52. Many examples of GWR, LMS, LNER and BR coaches are in regular use, as are many of the 100 wagons. Future plans include installing a turntable at Bridgnorth and providing covered accommodation for historic coach sets and locomotives awaiting overhaul. The railway has featured in many cinema and TV films, including the 1979 version of John Buchan's *The Thirty Nine Steps*.

Skegness Electric Tramway

Tram Depot
Princes Parade
Skegness
Lincs

Tel: 01472 604657
Route: Tower Esplanade to Princes Parade
Length: 600yd
Gauge: 12¹/₄in
Open: Telephone for details

Opened in 1994 the Skegness Electric Tramway runs along the trackbed of the original seaside miniature railway which was closed in 1992. The line was still being developed and extended during the winter of 1995/6. A double-deck, battery-powered, bogie tramway car operates the service, by the side of the boating lake and children's paddling pool.

Snibston Discovery Park

Ashby Road
Coalville
Leics LE67 3LN

Tel: 01530 510851
Open: Daily except Christmas. Railway not yet in operation
Facilities: Car park, shop, refreshments, picnic site

A large open air industrial museum situated on the site of the former Snibston Colliery, opened in 1833 by George Stephenson. The remaining ¹/₄-mile length of track is part of the former colliery sidings and branch from the main Leicester and Burton line into the colliery. Exhibits displayed include examples of transport, engineering, mining and textiles. Locomotives include Hunslet 0-6-0 saddle tank No. 3851 *Cadley Hill No.1*, built in 1962, and Andrew Barclay 0-4-0 fireless No. 1815, built in 1924. Future plans include eventual completion of the railway layout and extension across the site to the end of the former colliery siding area and the running of a 2ft 6in gauge battery-operated colliery train.

Somerleyton Hall Miniature Railway

Somerleyton Hall
Somerleyton
Nr Lowestoft
Suffolk

Route: Within grounds of Somerleyton Hall
Length: ¹/₄ mile
Gauge: 7¹/₄in
Open: Sundays, Thursdays and bank holiday Monday afternoons mid April to early October, Tuesdays and Wednesdays in July and August

Southwold Museum

Victoria Street
Southwold
Suffolk

Tel: 01502 722375
Open: Daily Spring Bank Holiday to end September

This local museum collection includes many small relics and photographs of the much lamented Southwold Railway. This 3ft gauge line ran the 8³/₄ miles from Halesworth to Southwold and was opened in 1879. It was finally closed to all traffic in 1929, though the railway company itself was not finally wound up until 1989.

Stapleford Park Miniature Railway

Stapleford Park
Nr Melton Mowbray
Leicestershire

Tel: 01572 787522
Route: Within grounds of Stapleford Park
Length: 2 miles
Gauge: 10¹/₄in
Open: Special events only. Telephone for details

This famous miniature railway was originally opened by the late Lord Gretton in 1958 and during its peak years included four stations. When Lord Gretton died in 1983 the railway was closed and put into storage. More recently the line has been redesigned and equipment restored. It was temporarily re-opened to the public in 1995. American-style steam locomotives used on the railway included two 'Atlantic' 4-4-2s and a 2-8-4, plus a Ford Cortina-powered 'Warship' class diesel. Regular services are not planned at the present time and interested parties should make contact first by telephone.

Strumpshaw Hall Steam Museum

Strumpshaw
Norwich
Norfolk

Tel: 01603 712339
Open: Daily except Saturdays mid July to early October

Included in this museum collection of working agricultural equipment is a short operating narrow gauge railway. 15in loco *Cagney* is a static exhibit.

Right GWR 0-6-0PT No. 5764 at Arley station on the Severn Valley Railway *(AA Photo Library)*

Telford Steam Railway

The Old Loco Shed
Horsehay
Telford TF4 2LT

Tel: 01952 503880
Open: Weekends, telephone for details

The Telford Horsehay Steam Trust was founded in 1976 to restore locomotives and rolling stock. It is planned to operate these on the Horsehay to Lightmoor branch, part of the former GWR line from Wellington to Buildwas which closed in 1964. Services along ½-mile of track started in 1984 and a ¼-mile length of 2ft gauge tramway was opened in 1991. Locomotives on the site include GWR 0-6-2 tank No. 5619 and several industrial steam and diesel examples.

The Village

Fleggburgh
Burgh St Margaret
Great Yarmouth
Norfolk NR29 3AF

Tel: 01493 369770
Route: Within site of heritage museum
Length: 1 mile
Gauge: 2ft
Open: Daily February to end October
Facilities: Car park, refreshments, museum

A heritage village museum with a collection of steam engines and fairground rides. A 2ft narrow gauge railway, built in 1986, operates with two steam-outline diesel locomotives and a mixture of open and closed coaches. The route is circular around the Village and has carriage sidings and engine shed. A goods siding serves the steam-driven sawmill. Restored Swedish standard gauge 2-6-4 tank No. 1928 is on static display.

Opposite Garratt 2-6-0+0-6-2 *Norfolk Hero* at work on the Wells & Walsingham Light Railway *(Mike Esau)*

112

Walsall Arboretum Railway

Walsall Arboretum Extension
Broadway North
Walsall
West Midlands

Route: Pathways Station to Arboretum Central
Length: ¾ mile
Gauge: 7¼in
Open: Every Sunday and bank holiday afternoons all year.
Facilities: Car park

This double track miniature railway is operated entirely by volunteers along the northern edge of the Arboretum Extension. It was originally opened as a single track line in 1976 and slowly expanded to its present out-and-back layout. Locomotives in regular use include Romulus 0-4-0 and GWR 2-6-2 steam locomotives, a 'Hymek' battery electric and a petrol hydraulic 0-4-0 shunter. Visiting locomotives are a regular feature on the line, which includes a terminus station, turntables and workshop.

Wells & Walsingham Light Railway

Wells-next-the-Sea
Norfolk NR23 1RB

Tel: 01328 856506 (talking timetable)
Route: Wells-next-the-Sea to Little Walsingham
Length: 4 miles
Gauge: 10¼in
Open: Daily Good Friday to end September
Facilities: Car park, shop, refreshments

The longest 10¼in gauge railway in the world also operates the most powerful steam locomotive of that gauge – a 20ft-long 'Garratt' 2-6-0+0-6-2 *Norfolk Hero*, built in 1986. This unique little line, owned built and operated by retired naval commander Roy Francis, opened in 1982 on the trackbed of the old standard gauge Wells & Fakenham Railway which opened in 1857 and was closed by BR in 1964. An 0-6-0 tank engine, *Pilgrim*, operated services from opening until

1986. Intermediate halts are provided at Warham St Mary and Wighton, and a former Great Eastern Railway signalbox, originally sited at Swainsthorpe, has been preserved at Wells station where it is used as a shop and tearoom.

Wells Harbour Railway

Beach Road
Wells-next-the-Sea
Norfolk

Tel: 01328 878871
Route: Wells Harbour to Pinewoods Caravan Park
Length: 1 mile
Gauge: 10¼in
Open: Easter to September. Telephone for details
Facilities: Car park, refreshments, picnic site

A frequent service of miniature trains operates between the caravan park and harbour in the town of Wells. Motive power is provided by one 0-4-2T steam locomotive and one petrol locomotive.

Weston Park Railway

Weston Park
Weston-under-Lizard
Shifnal
Shropshire TF11 8LE

Tel: 01952 850207
Route: Within grounds of stately home
Length: 1½ miles
Gauge: 7¼in
Open: Weekends and bank holidays Easter to September, weekdays June to August

This well constructed miniature railway which passes through woodland and alongside lakes within the grounds of Weston Park, a 17th century mansion now run as a hotel, employs four narrow gauge steam and two diesel locomotives. The railway was built for continual running using track and some of the motive power from the former Hilton Valley Miniature Railway, near Bridgnorth.

Northern England and the Isle of Man

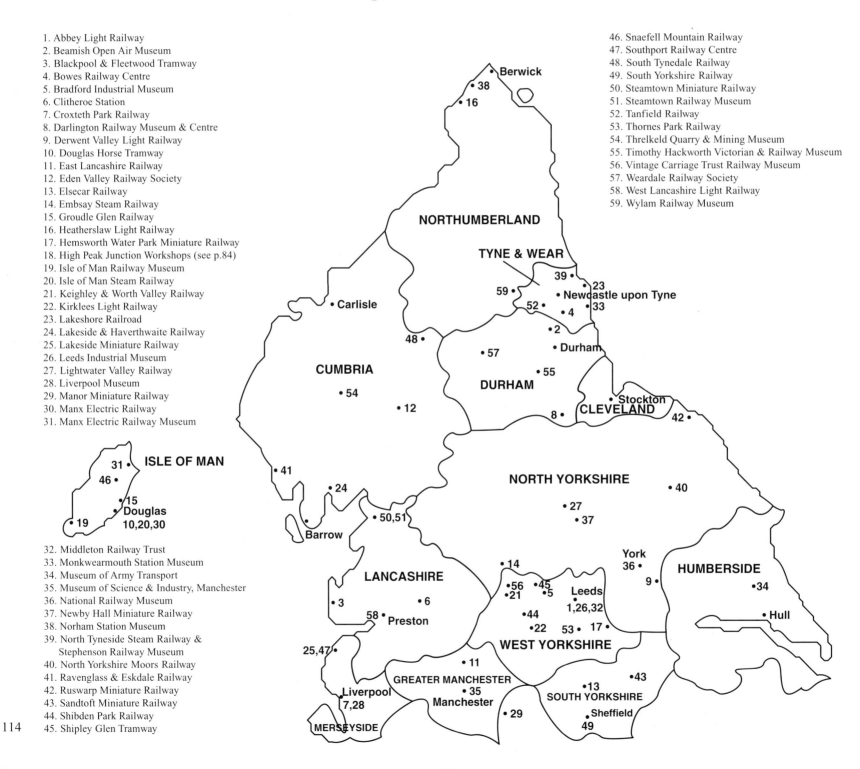

1. Abbey Light Railway
2. Beamish Open Air Museum
3. Blackpool & Fleetwood Tramway
4. Bowes Railway Centre
5. Bradford Industrial Museum
6. Clitheroe Station
7. Croxteth Park Railway
8. Darlington Railway Museum & Centre
9. Derwent Valley Light Railway
10. Douglas Horse Tramway
11. East Lancashire Railway
12. Eden Valley Railway Society
13. Elsecar Railway
14. Embsay Steam Railway
15. Groudle Glen Railway
16. Heatherslaw Light Railway
17. Hemsworth Water Park Miniature Railway
18. High Peak Junction Workshops (see p.84)
19. Isle of Man Railway Museum
20. Isle of Man Steam Railway
21. Keighley & Worth Valley Railway
22. Kirklees Light Railway
23. Lakeshore Railroad
24. Lakeside & Haverthwaite Railway
25. Lakeside Miniature Railway
26. Leeds Industrial Museum
27. Lightwater Valley Railway
28. Liverpool Museum
29. Manor Miniature Railway
30. Manx Electric Railway
31. Manx Electric Railway Museum

46. Snaefell Mountain Railway
47. Southport Railway Centre
48. South Tynedale Railway
49. South Yorkshire Railway
50. Steamtown Miniature Railway
51. Steamtown Railway Museum
52. Tanfield Railway
53. Thornes Park Railway
54. Threlkeld Quarry & Mining Museum
55. Timothy Hackworth Victorian & Railway Museum
56. Vintage Carriage Trust Railway Museum
57. Weardale Railway Society
58. West Lancashire Light Railway
59. Wylam Railway Museum

32. Middleton Railway Trust
33. Monkwearmouth Station Museum
34. Museum of Army Transport
35. Museum of Science & Industry, Manchester
36. National Railway Museum
37. Newby Hall Miniature Railway
38. Norham Station Museum
39. North Tyneside Steam Railway &
    Stephenson Railway Museum
40. North Yorkshire Moors Railway
41. Ravenglass & Eskdale Railway
42. Ruswarp Miniature Railway
43. Sandtoft Miniature Railway
44. Shibden Park Railway
45. Shipley Glen Tramway

Abbey Light Railway

Bridge Road
Kirkstall
Leeds LS5 3BW

Tel: 0113 2675087
Route: Kirkstall Abbey to Bridge Road
Length: 1/4 mile
Gauge: 2ft
Open: Sunday and bank holiday afternoons and
first Saturday in July

Founded in 1976 as a family railway and
supported by volunteers to restore vintage narrow
gauge railway locomotives and rolling stock. The
Abbey Light Railway opened for passengers in
1986. A well equipped machine shop is able to
carry out heavy repairs and construction of new
equipment from 10¼in to 2ft gauges. A collection
of 12 petrol and diesel industrial narrow gauge
locomotives are either being used or restored,
including examples dating back to 1917 and the
1920s. Rolling stock includes 'V' skips,
ammunition wagons and air-braked coaches. The
journey takes passengers from Bridge Road
through a landscaped area, over a mill race and up
to a wooded area in a cutting to Kirkstall Abbey.
Future plans include the construction of a 1920s
narrow gauge loading dock and turntable, and the
building of a Kerr Stuart 'Wren' class steam
locomotive.

Beamish Open Air Museum

Beamish
Co Durham DH9 0RG

Tel: 01207 231811
Open: Daily April to October, except Mondays
and Fridays November to March
Facilities: Car park, shop, refreshments, picnic
site

A very large, 200-acre, open air museum of late
19th century life in Northern England. Exhibits
include completely re-created houses, shops,
school, farm and colliery. There is much of

Lister 0-4-0 diesel No. 20449, built in 1942, at Kirkstall Abbey on the 2ft gauge Abbey Light Railway
(Abbey Light Railway)

railway interest including a range of typical North
Eastern Railway buildings, including the 1867
Rowley station (reconstructed at Beamish after
being moved from its site near Newcastle), goods
shed and signalbox and a short length of line.
Locomotives on display include a full-size replica
of the famous Stockton & Darlington Railway
Locomotion, NER Class C1 0-6-0 No. 876 built
in 1889, and several ancient industrial steam
examples. A 1½-mile electric tramway runs
through the site.

Blackpool & Fleetwood Tramway

Blackpool Transport Services
Rigby Road
Blackpool
Lancs FY1 5DD

Tel: 01253 23931
Route: South Shore Blackpool to Fleetwood
Ferry
Length: 11½ miles
Gauge: Standard
Open: Daily

One of Blackpool's biggest tourist attractions, this
street tramway is the only survivor of systems that
were once widespread in the towns and cities of
Britain. It was originally opened in 1898 and
electric power is taken from overhead lines. Over
80 electric trams operate an intensive service
along the sea front. Examples include vintage and
veteran single and double-deck tramcars. During
Blackpool Illuminations each autumn the trams
are decorated with coloured lights.

Bowes Railway Centre

Springwell Village
Nr Gateshead
Tyne & Wear NE9 7QJ

Tel: 0191 4161847
Open: Operating days on first and third Sunday of
each month Easter to September, bank holiday
Mondays. Static viewing on other Sundays
Facilities: Car park, shop, refreshments, brakevan
rides, demonstration trains

The Bowes Railway was designed by George
Stephenson as a colliery line and opened in 1826.
It was built to carry coal from collieries along its
length to Jarrow on the River Tyne for shipment.
The line passed into the ownership of the Bowes
family in 1850, which operated it until collieries
were nationalised in 1947. It used a mixture of
rope-worked inclines and locomotive-hauled
sections, and operated virtually unchanged until
1974. It is now a scheduled Ancient Monument
and the centre at Springwell includes the only
working rope-hauled standard gauge incline in
the world. Preservation began in 1975 and
visitors can now travel in steam-hauled brakevans
along a short length of track from the engineering
centre and up the east incline to Blackham's Hill,
where they alight to visit the rope haulage
buildings and watch rope demonstrations. Future
plans include an extension, due to open in 1996,
from Blackham's Hill to Wrekenton along the
line's old Pelaw main railway branch. The centre
also houses the largest collection of colliery
rolling stock in the country, several steam and
diesel locomotives and the restored 19th-century
railway workshops.

Bradford Industrial Museum

Moorside Mills
Moorside Road
Bradford
West Yorkshire BD2 3HP

Tel: 01274 631756
Open: Daily except Mondays

Restored Clitheroe station on the Blackburn to Hellifield line *(Ribble Valley Borough Council)*

Facilities: Refreshments, shop, horse-drawn tram
rides, facilities for disabled

This industrial museum, situated in a former
wool-spinning mill built in 1875, houses a large
collection of stationary steam and gas engines,
and a transport section which includes road
vehicles, a Hudswell-Clarke 0-4-0 saddle tank
locomotive built in 1922, and the last surviving
Bradford tramcar and trolley bus. Visitors can
take rides on a horse-drawn tramway.

Clitheroe Station

Clitheroe
Lancashire

Tel: 01200 452556
Open: Monday to Saturday
Facilities: Art gallery, booking office, waiting
room

Clitheroe station, dating from 1870, is situated on
the former Lancashire & Yorkshire Railway's
Blackburn to Hellifield line. Passenger services
ceased in 1962, but in 1994 a regular weekday
service was reintroduced between here and
Manchester. In addition the old railway station
building, now in private ownership and leased to
the Ribble Valley Borough Council, has been
completely restored to its Victorian glory. The
'Platform Gallery' is a valuable venue for local
artists to exhibit their work.

Croxteth Park Railway

Croxteth Hall Estate
Liverpool

Route: Within park
Length: 600yd
Gauge: 7¼in
Open: Easter to September with steam operations
on certain Sundays

The miniature railway operates around an oval
with one station, Croxteth Halt, and is enclosed
by high fences. Three steam locomotives,
including *Dennis* and *Estelle*, and one petrol
engine operate the trains.

Darlington Railway Museum & Centre

North Road Station
Darlington
Co Durham DL3 6ST

Tel: 01325 460532
Open: Daily except Christmas and New Year
Facilities: Car park, shop, refreshments, facilities for disabled

North Road station was built in 1842 for the Stockton & Darlington Railway. The railway museum and restoration centre is housed in the restored station building, goods shed and the Hopetown Carriage Works. Exhibits include the original SDR *Locomotion* built in 1825 and 0-6-0 *Derwent* built in 1845, as well as two North Eastern Railway 2-4-0s and several industrial locomotives. Historic rolling stock on display includes a SDR coach built in 1846 and a NER example built in 1860. Steam train rides, on selected days only, are provided on a short length of line within the site. North Road station, with its overall roof, is still used by Regional Railways trains operating on the Darlington to Bishop Auckland service.

Derwent Valley Light Railway

Murton Park
Murton Lane
Murton
York YO1 3UF

Tel: 01904 489966
Route: Within station site
Length: 1/2 mile
Gauge: Standard
Open: Weekends May to October (diesel), bank holiday Sundays and Mondays (steam), and December. Telephone for details
Facilities: Car park, shop, refreshments, facilities for disabled

The original Derwent Valley Light Railway, an independent company, opened in 1913 and ran for

Tramcar No. 35 on the Douglas Horse Tramway *(Julian Holland)*

16 miles from Layerthorpe in York to Cliffe Common, just outside Selby. Services were originally mixed traffic but passenger services ceased in 1926. Closure of the line to goods traffic was in stages – up to Elvington in 1968, to Dunnington in 1973 with final closure of the remainder in 1982. During World War II the railway was heavily used by the War Department as a supply route to the airfields at Elvington, Skipwith and the depot at Wheldrake. The 1/2-mile section that remains runs from Murton Lane to the Osbaldwick road. The railway has been run since 1990 by the Great Yorkshire Railway Preservation Society and is based on a site at the former DVLR station at Murton Lane which also houses the Yorkshire Museum of Farming and a reconstructed Viking village. Locomotives working and on display include two industrial steam saddle tanks and six diesels together with a small collection of rolling stock. An award-winning restored former North Eastern Railway signalbox, originally situated at Murton, is also open to visitors.

Douglas Horse Tramway

Derby Castle
Douglas
Isle of Man

Tel: 01624 663366
Route: Derby Castle to Victoria Pier
Length: 1 1/2 miles
Gauge: 3ft
Open: Daily May to late September
Facilities: Limited parking, shop, small museum

Opened in 1876 by Thomas Lightfoot this horse-drawn tramway has been in continuous operation, apart from temporary closure during World War II, ever since. It was sold in 1882 to The Isle of Man Tramways Ltd and then again to the Isle of Man Tramways & Electric Power Co Ltd in 1894. As a result of the failure of Dumbell's Bank in 1900 the Douglas Corporation bought the tramway from the liquidator for £50,000, and the Corporation continues to run the system to this

day. A total of 21 tramcars, dating from 1883 to 1913, are used on this service on the double track road tramway along Douglas Promenade. Stables for the 38 working horses are situated at Derby Castle and are open to visitors. In winter the horses are put to grazing at various parts of the island. Future plans include running illuminated trams in 1996 to celebrate the Douglas Corporation Centenary, and the building of a visitor centre at the stables.

East Lancashire Railway

Bolton Street Station
Bury
Lancashire BL9 0EY

Tel: 0161 7647790
Route: Bury to Rawtenstall
Length: 8 miles
Gauge: Standard
Open: Weekends all year, bank holidays Easter to end August, weekdays in August
Facilities: Car park, shop, refreshments, picnic site, Wine & Dine train, footplate driving experience, facilities for disabled

The original East Lancashire Railway came into being as early as 1846 to serve cotton mills in the Irwell Valley north of Bury. The line was extended to Bacup in 1852 and the railway was absorbed by the Lancashire & Yorkshire in 1859 and then the LNWR in 1922, before becoming part of the LMS in 1923 and closing to all traffic in 1980. A preservation group had previously moved in to Bury and subsequently opened a transport museum in 1969. After financial assistance, exceeding £1 million, from the local councils and county council, first public trains started running between Bury and Ramsbottom in 1987, with Rawtenstall being reached in 1991. Work is now progressing on an eastward link from Bury to Heywood, where the ELR will connect with the main rail system. Trains are operated along the picturesque Irwell Valley, with

Left L&Y 0-6-0 No. 52129 on the East Lancashire Railway, October 27 1995 *(Mike Esau)*

Avonside 0-6-0ST No. 1917 and train on the Elsecar Railway *(Elsecar Railway)*

its several viaducts, by a variety of preserved main line steam and diesel locomotives. Steam locomotives include GWR 'Manor' class 4-6-0 No. 7828 *Odney Manor*, LMS Class 5MT 4-6-0 No. 45337 and BR Class 9F 2-10-0 No. 92207. Visiting locomotives from other railways can frequently be seen in action and the ELR has built up a reputation for its varied collection of preserved diesels which can be seen in action on several diesel weekends. Preserved main line diesels include examples from Classes 01, 05, 08, 14, 24, 25, 31, 35, 40, 42, 45, 50 and 52.

Eden Valley Railway Society

c/o David Greenhaigh
Hillcroft
Coleby
Appleby
Cumbria CA16 6BD

The Society was inaugurated in October 1995 with the aim of purchasing and restoring the remains of the old North Eastern Railway line (originally built by the Stockton & Darlington Railway) from Appleby to Warcop, on the former Darlington to Penrith route across the Pennines. In the more distant future the Society will be looking at development of the line eastwards from Warcop. For more details contact the above address.

Elsecar Railway

Wath Road
Elsecar
Barnsley
South Yorkshire S7 8HJ

Tel: 01226 740203
Route: Elsecar Workshop to Cortonwood Colliery
Length: 2 miles
Gauge: Standard
Open: Most weekends and Wednesdays. Telephone for details
Facilities: Car park, shop, refreshments, industrial museum, facilities for disabled

The Elsecar Railway is situated in a large open air industrial archaeology museum which incorporates the old Elsecar Ironworks. The Elsecar workshops were once the hub of industrial activity on the Wentworth Estate for the mining and engineering enterprises of the Earl Fitzwilliam of Wentworth Woodhouse. The workshops were built between 1850 and 1860 and were taken over by the NCB in 1947 before finally closing in the early 1980s. The Elsecar branch of the South Yorkshire Railway opened in 1850 and the single track line ran through Mexborough across the Dearne & Dove Canal by lifting bridge. It carried mineral traffic serving the collieries and ironworks and when Cortonwood Colliery closed in 1984 the track was lifted. The present railway employs Avonside 0-6-0 saddle tank No. 1917, built in 1924, with three ex-BR coaches and conveys passengers from the former workshop site through an attractive conservation area beside a branch of the Dearne & Dove Canal to the old Cortonwood Colliery.

Embsay Steam Railway

Embsay Station
Embsay
Skipton
Yorkshire BD23 6AX

Tel: 01756 794727/01756 795189
Route: Embsay to Holywell
Length: 2¹/₂ miles
Gauge: Standard
Open: Steam trains – Sundays all year, Tuesdays and Saturdays in July, daily end July to end August. Diesel trains – Saturdays in June and September
Facilities: Car park, shop. refreshments, museum, picnic site, Wine & Dine train, facilities for disabled

The former Midland Railway branch from Skipton to Ilkley opened in 1888 and was closed by BR in 1965. The Yorkshire Dales Railway obtained a Light Railway Order in 1979 and since then has re-opened 2¹/₂ miles of track from Embsay, with its original Midland Railway buildings, to its current terminus at Holywell. Work is now progressing well on the line eastwards to the tourist centre of Bolton Abbey where a new station is being built. The railway owns and operates a very large collection of finely restored industrial steam locomotives and diesels.

Groudle Glen Railway

Groudle Glen
Onchan
Isle of Man

Tel: 01624 622138 (evenings)
Route: Lhen Coan to Sea Lion Rocks
Length: ³/₄ mile
Gauge: 2ft
Open: Sundays and bank holidays
Facilities: Shop, picnic site

Opened by R M Broadbent in 1896 to take visitors from a glen to a rocky headland, where sea lions and polar bears were kept in a dammed sea inlet, this narrow gauge railway was an immediate success. Trains were operated by a 2-4-0 steam locomotive *Sea Lion*, built by Bagnall in 1896, and in 1905 a second engine *Polar Bear*, arrived. After World War I battery locomotives operated the trains but six years later the steam locomotives returned. Following closure during World War II, services ran from 1950 until closure in 1962. Restoration of the line began in 1982 by the Isle of Man Steam Railway Supporters' Association and in 1986 the line partly re-opened, with trains being hauled by two Hunslet diesel locomotives. *Sea Lion* was rescued in a semi-derelict condition from Loughborough and fully restored by instructors and apprentices of the BNFL Training Centre at Sellafield, before returning to service in 1987. Complete restoration of passenger services to Sea Lion Rocks was completed in 1992. A replica Bagnall tank locomotive with a boiler similar to *Sea Lion* is currently being built for use on the line.

Bagnall 2-4-0T *Sea Lion*, built 1896, at Lhen Coan on the Groudle Glen Railway
(Groudle Glen Railway/A J Proctor)

Heatherslaw Light Railway

Ford Forge
Heatherslaw
Cornhill-on-Tweed
Northumberland TD12 4QA

Tel: 01890 820244/01890 820317
Route: Heatherslaw Mill to Etal village
Length: 1³/₄ miles
Gauge: 15in
Open: Daily Easter to end October, except
Fridays in October
Facilities: Car park, shop, refreshments, picnic
site, model railway, engine driving courses,
facilities for disabled

Situated on the Heatherslaw Estate, with its
restored water-mill and blacksmith's forge, this
miniature railway was built from scratch in 1989
and follows the picturesque River Till with trains
operated by 0-4-2 steam locomotive *Lady
Augusta*, built in 1989, and a Perkins diesel used
for maintenance. Passengers are carried in a
variety of disc-braked coaches, all built in the
railway's workshops. Future line extensions and a
new home-built steam engine are planned.

Hemsworth Water Park Miniature Railway

Hoyle Road
Kinsley
Pontefract
West Yorkshire

Tel: 01977 615865
Route: Within water park
Length: 300yd
Gauge: 7¹/₄in
Open: February school holiday week, then
weekends and all school holidays to end October
Facilities: Car park, extensive leisure features
within whole park, facilities for disabled

Situated in the Playworld section of the large
Hemsworth Water Park, this miniature railway
was built in 1993 with help from members of the

0-4-2T *Lucy* on the 7¹/₄in gauge Hemsworth Water Park Miniature Railway *(Hemsworth Water Park Miniature Railway)*

Wakefield Model Engineers Society. The total
circuit, which includes engine shed and turntable,
includes a 1-in-80 gradient. Operating the trains
are steam locomotive 0-4-2 *Lucy* and petrol
hydraulic 0-4-2 *Christopher.*

High Peak Junction Workshops

High Peak Junction
Nr Cromford
Derbyshire

Tel: 01629 825208/01629 823204
Open: Daily Easter to September and winter
weekends
Facilities: Car park, shop, museum, refreshments,
picnic site

The former workshops of the Cromford & High
Peak Railway, opened in 1830 and closed by BR
in 1967, have been restored to a museum of local
transport interest. The railway was built to link
the adjacent Cromford Canal with the Peak Forest
Canal at Whaley Bridge. and was built on canal
building principles. Instead of locks to climb hills
the engineers used steep inclines, each worked by
a steam-powered beam engine, to haul the wagons
up the gradients. The workshops were built in

1825/26 and have been preserved in their original
state and include a railway exhibition and video
programme. The 17¹/₂-mile High Peak Trail now
covers the route of the old trackbed from High
Peak Junction to Dowlow near Buxton. The
nearby restored engine houses at Middleton Top
and Leawood with their early 19th-century beam
engine can be seen in action on certain days in the
summer.

Isle of Man Railway Museum

Strand Road
Port Erin
Isle of Man

Tel: 01624 663366

The museum of the Isle of Man Railways is
situated adjacent to the station at Port Erin.
Exhibits include Beyer Peacock 2-4-0 steam
locomotives *Sutherland*, built in 1873, and
Mannin built in 1926 and a unique six-wheeled
Manx Northern Railway carriage, the Royal
Saloon, the Duke of Sutherland's carriage as well
as other IOMR artefacts and ephemera.

Isle of Man Steam Railway

Strathallan Crescent
Douglas
Isle of Man IM2 4NR

Tel: 01624 663366
Route: Douglas to Port Erin
Length: 15¹/₂ miles
Gauge: 3ft
Open: Easter and daily May to end September
Facilities: Car parks, shop, refreshments, facilities
for disabled

Part of the once extensive Isle of Man Railway's
narrow gauge system, this line was opened in
1874 and has been in more or less continuous use
since then. Nationalisation by the Manx
Government in 1977 saved this section from
certain closure. The Victorian atmosphere still
pervades the whole line, from its beautifully

Beyer-Peacock 2-4-0T No. 11 *Maitland*, built in 1905, awaiting its next turn of duty at Douglas, Isle of Man Steam Railway *(Julian Holland)*

maintained station buildings to the vintage locomotives and carriages. A journey along the line, with its rolling Manx scenery and glimpses of the Irish Sea, is like taking a trip back in time to a period 100 years ago when the pace of life was less frenetic. The oldest locomotive on the books is Beyer Peacock 2-4-0T No. 4 *Loch*, built in 1874, and the railway is also home to two diesel railcars from the former Donegal Railway Company in Ireland. Locomotive No. 15 *Caledonia*, an 0-6-0T built by Dubs in 1885, was fully restored to working order to celebrate the centenary of the opening of the Snaefell Mountain Railway in 1995 (see p.134). Major celebrations are planned for 1998 to celebrate 125 years of passenger steam trains on the island.

Keighley & Worth Valley Railway

Haworth Station
Keighley
West Yorkshire BD22 8NJ

Tel: 01535 645214/01535 647777 (talking timetable)
Route: Keighley to Oxenhope
Length: 5 miles
Gauge: Standard
Open: Weekends all year. Monday to Friday Easter week, Spring bank holiday, July, August, October half term and Boxing Day to New Year's Day
Facilities: Car parks, shops, refreshments, museums, Wine & Dine trains, facilities for disabled

This was one of the earliest preserved standard gauge railways, re-opened by a preservation society in 1967. The railway still serves the community of the Worth Valley as originally intended. The former Midland Railway branch from Keighley, on the main Leeds to Skipton line, to Oxenhope opened in 1867 to serve the large number of local mills, and was closed by BR in 1962. The line, although short, offers much to the

visitor together with its associations with the Brontes at Haworth and the filming of E Nesbit's *The Railway Children* at Oakworth. A large collection of nearly 40 steam and diesel locomotives has been built up over the years and the railway is also home to two museums, The Vintage Carriage Trust at Ingrow (see p.141) and the Railway Museum at Oxenhope, and extensive workshop facilities. Locomotives range from Lancashire & Yorkshire Railway 0-6-0ST No. 752, built in 1881, former BR Standard Class 4MT 2-6-4 tank No. 80002 to LMS 'Jubilee' class 4-6-0 No. 45596 *Bahamas*, built in 1935. Steam trains operate most of the services along this picturesque route calling at carefully restored award-winning gas-lit stations. Tiny Damems station is reputably the smallest in Britain.

Kirklees Light Railway

The Railway Station
Park Mill Way
Clayton West
Nr Huddersfield
West Yorkshire HP8 9PE

Tel: 01484 865727
Route: Clayton West to Skelmanthorpe
Length: 2 miles
Gauge: 15in
Open: Weekends and bank holidays all year, daily Spring bank holiday to end August
Facilities: Car park, refreshments, model railway.

This miniature railway operates along part of the trackbed of the former Lancashire & Yorkshire Railway's branch from Clayton West Junction to Clayton West, opened in 1879 and finally closed by BR in 1983. The Kirklees Light Railway was the brainchild of Brian Taylor who was also involved in the building of a 10¼in gauge miniature steam railway at Shibden Park, Halifax. After several years of searching for a suitable site, work started on the present line in 1990, the first

Right LMS 0-6-0T No. 47279 enters Oakworth station on the Keighley & Worth Valley Railway, September 11 1994 *(Mike Esau)*

Above 2-6-2T *Fox* at Clayton West, Kirklees Light Railway *(N R Knight)*

Route: Haverthwaite to Lakeside
Length: 3¹/₂ miles
Gauge: Standard
Open: Easter to early November. Telephone for details
Facilities: Car park, shop, refreshments, picnic site

The former Furness Railway branch from Ulverston to Lakeside, opened in 1869, was finally closed by BR in 1967. A preservation group took over the steeply-graded section from Haverthwaite and steam trains started running again in 1973 when the line was opened by the Bishop of Wakefield, the Rt Rev Eric Treacy. The short but highly scenic journey can be taken in conjunction with a 10¹/₂-mile trip along Lake Windermere as trains connect with steamers at Lakeside terminus. A collection of restored industrial and ex-BR steam and diesel locomotives are used on the line with the main motive power being two LMS designed and BR built 2-6-4 tank engines, Nos. 42073 and 42085, dating from 1950 and 1951 respectively.

train ran to Cuckoo's Nest in 1991 and to Skelmanthorpe in late 1992. Locomotives operating on the line include Hunslet-type 2-6-2 tank *Fox* and 0-6-4 saddle tank *Badger*. Rolling stock consists of nine 20-seat carriages, the fully enclosed examples being heated. All locomotives and rolling stock were built for the railway by Brian Taylor who has built and continues to supply equipment for other railways. Work is already in progress to complete the further two miles of the branch line to Clayton West Junction. Clayton West is also home to the Barnsley Society of Model Engineers, who operate a passenger-carrying miniature railway on most weekends.

Lakeshore Railroad

South Marine Park
South Shields
Tyne & Wear

Route: Within park
Length: 555yd

Gauge: 9¹/₂in
Open: Weekends and school holidays Easter to November, daily June to August

Opened in 1972 this miniature railway runs around the perimeter of a boating lake and passes through woodland. Developments have included construction of a station and water tower and a two-train service is in operation on bank holidays and some Sundays in July and August. Steam locomotives operating are a ¹/₆ scale Atcheson, Topeka & Santa Fe 4-6-2, No. 3440, and a ¹/₄ scale Ferrocarril National del Magdalena Columbia 2-6-2 No. 27. A new ¹/₆ scale Wabash Railroad 4-6-4 is under construction. Passengers are carried on a total of nine toast rack coaches.

Lakeside & Haverthwaite Railway

Haverthwaite Station
Nr Ulverston
Cumbria LA12 8AL
Tel: 015395 31594

Lakeside Miniature Railway

Pleasureland Station
Southport
Merseyside

Tel: 01704 535796
Route: Within Marine Park
Length: ¹/₂ mile
Gauge: 15in
Open: Weekends during March, April and October, daily in summer season

This seaside miniature railway opened in 1911 and was extended to the beach in 1948. Most of the route runs alongside the Marine Lake from Pleasureland to the pier and beach. Motive power consists of steam locomotive, *Red Dragon,* three

Right Hunslet 0-6-0ST No. 11 *Repulse* approaches Newby Bridge Halt on the Lakeside & Haverthwaite Railway *(AA Photo Library)*

diesel electrics, *Prince Charles*, *Duke of Edinburgh* and *Golden Jubilee*, and diesel *Princess Anne*. Three sets of carriages provide seating for 72 passengers.

Leeds Industrial Museum

Armley Mills
Canal Road
Leeds LS12 2QF

Tel: 0113 2637861
Open: Tuesdays to Saturdays and Sunday afternoons
Facilities: Car park, shop, operating narrow gauge railway, facilities for disabled

This industrial museum, opened in 1982, is housed in a restored 19th-century water-powered textile mill and portrays the technology and industry of the city of Leeds. A large collection of railway items includes a locomotive display of steam, diesel and mine locomotives and an operating narrow gauge railway. On display are restored Manning Wardle 0-6-0 saddle tank No. 865 *Aldwyth*, battery electric No. 1210 *Greenwood & Batley*, Hudswell-Clarke 2-6-2 diesel *Junin* with 15 other steam, diesel and electric locomotives on view in unrestored condition. The mixed gauge (18in and 2ft) narrow gauge line runs for about 300yd from the locomotive gallery through the museum buildings and grounds to the weir on the River Aire. The line, used for demonstration purposes only, operates Hunslet 0-4-0 well tank No. 684 *Jack* and a Hudson-Hunslet 0-4-0 diesel.

Lightwater Valley Railway

Lightwater Valley Theme Park
North Stainley
Ripon
N Yorkshire HG4 3HT

Tel: 01765 635321
Route: Continuous loop within Theme Park
Length: 1 mile
Gauge: 15in

Open: Easter to October
Facilities: Normal theme park facilities

The railway is part of a large theme park and links many of the attractions. The line features three stations, a Victorian-style loco shed, two bridges and a tunnel. Motive power consists of three steam locomotives, *Yvette* (a 4-4-0 built in 1946), *Little Giant* (an 'Atlantic' 4-4-2 built in 1905 by Bassett-Lowke) and *John* (an 'Atlantic' 4-4-2 built in 1920), and one steam-outline diesel, *Rio Grande* built in 1979. Passengers travel in open and closed stock furnished with transverse seating. The engine shed at Lightwater houses an interesting collection of locomotives.

Liverpool Museum

William Brown Street
Liverpool L3 8EN

Tel: 0151 478 4399
Open: Weekdays, Sunday afternoons
Facilities: refreshments, shop, facilities for disabled

The transport section, opened in 1970, of this large museum houses various railway exhibits as well as many depicting the history of road transport. The most famous railway exhibit is 0-4-2 *Lion*, built in 1838 by Todd, Kitson & Laird of Leeds for the Liverpool & Manchester Railway. In 1859 *Lion* was sold to the Mersey Docks & Harbour Board where she was used as a stationary engine until 1928. She was acquired by the museum in 1965 and restored to full working order in 1979. It is planned to relocate the transport gallery to the Museum of Liverpool Life when the Liverpool Museum is refurbished.

Manor Miniature Railway

Manor Park
Glossop
Derbyshire

Route: Within park
Length: 1/2 mile

Gauge: 7¼in
Open: Sundays and bank holidays, summer Saturdays

The railway is laid with aluminium trackwork around Manor Park towards Old Glossop. The original layout was a continuous loop with a spur to the loco shed. It has since been rebuilt with connecting lines leading to a terminal station. Internal combustion locomotives are frequently used but visiting steam haulage can be also be seen.

Manx Electric Railway

Derby Castle Station
Douglas
Isle of Man

Tel: 01624 663366
Route: Douglas to Ramsey
Length: 17¾ miles
Gauge: 3ft
Open: Daily Easter to October
Facilities: Car parks, shop, refreshments, museum

The Manx Electric Railway opened between Douglas and Laxey in 1893 and the present line to Ramsey was opened in 1899. In operation ever since, it was nationalised by the Manx government in 1957, and still employs some of the original Victorian motor and trailer cars. The line is double track throughout, much of it on the roadside with many small tram stops, and electric power is taken from overhead lines. The journey from Douglas, where it connects with a sea front horse-drawn tramway (see p.117), to Ramsey is fascinating, firstly passing the Groudle Glen Railway (see p.120) before reaching the sylvan station at Laxey where it connects with the Snaefell Mountain Railway (see p.134). The section of line northwards entails a very steep climb from Laxey to the 550ft-high summit above Bulgham Bay, and skirts some breathtaking coastline, with fine views of the Irish Sea.

Right Manx Electric Railway car No. 33 and Snaefell Mountain Railway car No. 6 at Laxey station, Manx Electric Railway *(Julian Holland)*

Manx Electric Railway Museum

Ramsey Station
Ramsey
Isle of Man

Tel: 01624 663366
Open: Daily mid April to September

Opened in 1979 is a museum that includes trams, artefacts and photographs of the Manx Electric Railway as well as from the former nearby Ramsey Pier Railway. Highlights include a royal saloon from 1895, electric locomotive from 1900, bogie electric freight tram, maintenance equipment and various displays on electric railway history and Manx Electric Railways.

Below DSB 0-4-0WT No. 385 at work on the Middleton Railway *(AA Photo Library)*

Middleton Railway Trust

Moor Road
Leeds LS10 2JQ

Tel: 01532 710320
Route: Moor Road to Middleton Park
Length: 1¼ miles
Gauge: Standard
Open: Saturdays, Sundays and bank holidays April to October
Facilities: Car park, shop, museum, facilities for disabled

The Middleton Railway operates on the site of the first railway to obtain an Act of Parliament, in 1758, and which was originally built to a gauge of 4ft 1in. It was also the first railway to use steam haulage commercially and became, in 1960, the first standard gauge line to be run by a preservation group. An interesting collection of steam and diesel locomotives and rolling stock is housed on the line and in the museum, including North Eastern Railway Class Y7 0-4-0T No. 1310, built in 1891, and LNER Class Y1 0-4-0 vertical boiler Sentinel No. 54, built in 1933.

Monkwearmouth Station Museum

North Bridge Street
Sunderland
Tyne & Wear SR5 1AP

Tel: 0191 56770759
Open: Mondays to Saturdays and Sunday afternoons, except Christmas Day, New Year's Day, Boxing Day and Good Friday
Facilities: Shop, facilities for disabled

Monkwearmouth station is one of Britain's finest stations, built in an impressive neo-classical style in 1848 to mark the election of George Hudson (the 'Railway King') as the MP for Sunderland. The station was closed to passengers in 1967, although trains still pass beside the platform. Restored features include the booking office, unchanged since 1866, waiting shelter on the west platform and the siding area, housing restored rolling stock. The museum has a yearly series of changing exhibitions on transport themes, with a programme of holiday activities.

Museum of Army Transport

Flemingate
Beverley
North Humberside HU17 0NG

Tel: 01482 860445
Open: Daily except Christmas
Facilities: Car park, shop, refreshments, facilities for disabled

The Royal Corps of Transport museum includes a large collection covering Army rail, road and sea

Right The impressive Monkwearmouth station, now restored and used as a museum *(AA Photo Library)*

transport. The rail section, the only army railway museum in existence, is particularly extensive and includes a large archive section and a collection of exhibits from the famous Longmoor Military Railway in Hampshire which closed in 1971. Locomotives exhibited include 0-4-2 well tank *Gazelle*, built in 1893, 0-6-0 saddle tank *Woolmer*, built in 1910, and 2ft and 2ft 6in gauge Wickham Target Trolleys. The rolling stock displayed includes Lord Kitchener's 1885 carriage, a rail wrecker and a World War I armoured gun truck. A 2ft narrow gauge line, 200yds in length, gives passenger rides using World War II vintage Simplex locos. The line represents a World War I 'behind the trenches' system passing behind high banks of earth reminiscent of those days. Future extensions to this line are limited by the availability of 20lb Decauville track.

Museum of Science & Industry

Liverpool Road
Castlefield
Manchester M3 4FP

Tel: 0161 8321830/0161 8322244
Open: Daily except Christmas
Facilities: Car park, shop, refreshments, facilities for disabled

A science and industry museum situated in the original station buildings of the Liverpool & Manchester Railway, opened in 1830. In addition to the many and varied railway exhibits there is much to interest everyone, with displays on cotton mills, aviation, gas, electricity, space, water supply and sewage disposal. Railway exhibits, all built in Manchester, include Isle of Man Railway 2-4-0 tank No. 3 *Pender*, built by Beyer Peacock in 1873, a working replica (with some original parts) of the 1829 *Novelty*, South African Railways Class GL 3ft 6in gauge Garratt 4-8-2+2-8-4 No. 2352 and ex-BR Class EM2 electric Co-Co No. 1505 *Ariadne*, built in 1954. Steam train rides are given at weekends along nearly one mile of track within the museum complex and run past the original booking halls,

waiting room and warehouse. The latter is the oldest railway building in the world and houses various displays on Manchester's industrial and social history.

National Railway Museum

Leeman Road
York YO2 4XJ

Tel: 01904 621261
Open: Weekdays and Sundays except Christmas
Facilities: Car park, shop, refreshments, library

The National Collection, formed from the Clapham Collection and the North Eastern Railway Museum collection at York, opened in 1975 and is housed in two large halls, with the Great Hall opening in 1992. Railway technology is displayed around a central turntable in the Great Hall and exhibits range from the very early days of rail transport to the present. Over 60 restored British-built locomotives, steam, diesel and electric, are on view and include such historic examples as GWR *City of Truro*, BR *Evening Star* and the prototype 'Deltic' diesel. The South Hall contains 130 exhibits that illustrate travel by train with both passenger and goods trains lined up at platforms. These range from Queen Adelaide's royal saloon, built in 1842, a Lynton & Barnstaple Railway coach, built in 1897, a Wagons-Lits Night Ferry sleeping car, built in 1936, to numerous goods vehicles dating from 1815 to 1970. In addition there is a hands-on children's centre and an extensive library with photograph and drawing collections. Numerous other locomotives, some in full working order, and rolling stock are on loan to other museums and preserved railways throughout Britain. Future plans include developing the museum's conservation workshops with public access, and to develop the south garden to an attractive area with picnic site and miniature railway.

Newby Hall Miniature Railway

Newby Hall Estate
Ripon
N Yorkshire HG4 5AE

Tel: 01423 322583
Route: Within gardens of Newby Hall
Length: 1½ miles (return)
Gauge: 10¼in
Open: Daily, except Mondays, April to end September. Steam on Sundays and bank holiday Mondays
Facilities: Car park, stately home, gardens, refreshments

This miniature railway, which runs in the grounds of Newby Hall, was opened by Earl Mountbatten of Burma in 1971. The line runs for nearly one mile from a picturesque miniature station alongside the River Ure, giving good views of the house, gardens and orchards. The railway crosses a lifting steel bridge, two box-girder bridges and passes through a curving tunnel. A fine ⅕ scale model of an unrebuilt 'Royal Scot' class 4-6-0, built in 1950 by J Battinson, and a Western class diesel, *Countess de Grey*, built by Severn Lamb, operate the trains. Steam trains operate on Sundays only.

Norham Station Museum

Norham
Northumberland

Tel: 01289 382217
Open: Monday, Thursday and Saturday afternoons from May to September

This privately owned museum on the former North Eastern Railway branch from Tweedmouth to Kelso features the original signalbox, booking office and porter's room. The station, opened in 1849 and closed in 1965, now houses a museum, cared for by the last man to work at the station.

North Tyneside Steam Railway & Stephenson Railway Museum

Middle Engine Lane
West Chirton
North Shields
Tyne & Wear NE29 8DX

Tel: 0191 2622627
Open: Weekends Easter to September
Facilities: Car park, facilities for disabled

Both the museum and the railway share the same buildings, originally used as the Tyne & Wear Metro Test Centre. The museum displays the progress of railways with a collection of vintage and more modern steam, diesel and electric locomotives. Exhibits include Killingworth Colliery 0-4-0 *Billy* dating back to the early 19th century and Bo-Bo electric locomotive No. E4 built by Siemens in 1909. The standard gauge steam railway, 1³/₄-miles long, connects the Tyne & Wear Metro station at Percy Main with the site.

North Yorkshire Moors Railway

Pickering Station
Pickering
North Yorkshire YO18 7AJ

Tel: 01751 472508/01751 473535 (talking timetable)
Route: Grosmont to Pickering
Length: 18 miles
Gauge: Standard
Open: Daily April to October, December
Facilities: Car park, shop, refreshments, museum, Wine & Dine trains, picnic sites, railway trail, facilities for disabled

The present North Yorkshire Moors Railway was one of the earliest railways built in Britain. Engineered by George Stephenson it opened in 1836, along the route of an old turnpike road, and initially featured horse-drawn trains and a rope-

Right SR Class 'S15' 4-6-0 No. 30841 awaits to depart from Goathland on the North Yorkshire Moors Railway, September 2 1993 *(Mike Esau)*

hauled inclined plane. In 1845 it was taken over by George Hudson's York & North Midland Railway and was rebuilt and enlarged for steam operation. The North Eastern Railway bought the line in 1854, and in 1865 a new route was opened to bypass the 1,500yd-long 1-in-15 Beck Hole Incline, which was replaced by the 1-in-49 gradient between Grosmont and Goathland. Absorbed into the LNER in 1923 it was eventually closed by BR as a through route to Malton and York in 1965. The North Yorkshire Moors Railway Preservation Society took over part of the line in 1967 and in 1973 trains started running again on what is now the second-longest preserved railway in the country. A workshop and engine sheds have been established at Grosmont and trains are operated by a large collection of powerful main line steam and diesel locomotives. Locomotives include 0-6-2 Lambton tank No. 5, NER Class T3 0-8-0 No. 901, LNER Class K1 2-6-0 No. 2005, SR 'Schools' class 4-4-0 No. 30926 *Repton*, two LMS Class 5 4-6-0s, WD 2-10-0 No. 3672 *Dame Vera Lynn* and BR Standard Class 4MT 4-6-0 No. 75014 as well as several ex-BR diesels. A large and varied collection of rolling stock includes a Pullman set. NYMR trains connect with the main network at Grosmont, on the scenic Whitby to Middlesbrough Esk Valley line. A journey on the railway across the wild grandeur of the North Yorkshire Moors National Park to Pickering involves a steep climb to Goathland, known to TV addicts as Aidensfield in *Heartbeat*, before entering the picturesque Newtondale Gorge. The railway is frequently host to visiting locomotives from other preserved railways.

Ravenglass & Eskdale Railway

Ravenglass
Cumbria CA18 1SW

Tel: 01229 717171
Route: Ravenglass to Dalegarth
Length: 7 miles

Left 2-8-2 *River Mite* on the turntable at Dalegarth, Ravenglass & Eskdale Railway *(AA Photo Library)*

Gauge: 15in
Open: Daily end March to beginning November. Weekends in winter except Christmas
Facilities: Car parks, shop, refreshments, museum, picnic site, camping coaches, public house, facilities for disabled

The Ravenglass & Eskdale Railway opened in 1875 as a 3ft gauge line to carry haematite iron ore from mines in Eskdale to the Furness Railway at Ravenglass. The first locomotive was Manning Wardle 0-6-0 *Devon*. Passenger services started in 1876 but the company became bankrupt and was managed by a Receiver. Passenger trains stopped in 1908 and goods services ceased in 1913. However W J Bassett-Lowke, the famous manufacturer of model railways, came to the rescue and regauged the line to 15in. The first locomotive was 'Atlantic' 4-4-2 *Sans Pareil* and in 1915 trains ran again on what was the 'World's Smallest Public Railway'. A daily train service operated and an additional locomotive, 0-8-0 *Muriel* (later to become *River Irt* and converted to 0-8-2), was purchased from Sir Arthur Heywood. The line flourished with the growth of granite traffic and a new locomotive, 2-8-2 *River Esk*, was built. In 1925 the line was purchased by Sir Aubrey Brocklebank, who enlarged the quarries and stone crushing plant. Following the end of World War II the RER was purchased by the Keswick Granite Company in 1948 who closed the quarries and in 1960 the line was put up for sale by auction. However, an eleventh-hour rescue operation was mounted by railway enthusiasts and the line was saved again. In 1967 another locomotive, 2-8-2 *River Mite*, entered service and with improved revenues the railway has been progressively restored. The railway workshops constructed 2-6-2 *Northern Rock* in 1976 and have also built new diesel and steam locomotives for Blackpool Pleasure Beach and a Japanese leisure park. The RER also pioneered the use of radio for operation of their trains, a system that is now widely used by the main line railways. The headquarters of the line at Ravenglass, also home to the railway-owned 'Ratty Arms' public house and an interesting railway museum, is situated adjacent to the main

line railway station on the Cumbrian Coast Line. Six steam and six diesel locomotives operate on the line, and coaching stock consists of a mixture of open, semi-open and closed saloons.

Ruswarp Miniature Railway

The Carrs
Ruswarp
Nr Whitby
N Yorkshire YO21 1RL

Tel: 01947 604658
Route: Alongside River Esk
Length: ½ mile
Gauge: 7¼in
Open: Daily Easter week, weekends to Spring bank holiday, then daily to mid September
Facilities: Boat hire, car park, picnic site

Set in a picturesque setting alongside the River Esk, near Whitby, this miniature railway operates three steam locomotives - narrow gauge 2-6-2 *Mountaineer* and 2-4-2 *Danny* together with 4-6-0 LMS Class 5 *George Stephenson*.

Sandtoft Miniature Railway

Sandtoft Transport Centre
Belton Road
Sandtoft
Nr Doncaster
Yorkshire

Tel: 01724 711391
Route: Circular route within trolleybus museum
Length: ¼ mile
Gauge: 7¼in
Open: Easter to October. Telephone for details
Facilities: Car park, shop, refreshments, trolleybus rides, picnic site

Situated on a former RAF airfield, the centre houses a large collection of historic road vehicles, including working trolleybuses. A miniature passenger-carrying railway was opened in 1983 and operates within the trolleybus circuit. Trains are hauled by a 'Romulus' steam locomotive and

Cable-operated tramcars on the Shipley Glen Tramway *(M J Lock)*

This unique Victorian cable-operated tramway was opened in 1895. It was originally powered by a gas engine but converted to electric in 1928. The original winding equipment is still in use and part of it can be viewed in the museum. Two pairs of toast-rack coaches operate on two independent tracks which run uphill through woodland on a maximum gradient of 1-in-7. Slight curvature of the track prevents opposite ends from being viewed. The tramway serves Shipley Glen, famous for all its attractions including a children's funfair, countryside centre, tea garden, rock formations and the nearby factory village of Saltaire.

Snaefell Mountain Railway

Laxey Station
Laxey
Isle of Man

Tel: 01624 663366
Route: Laxey to Snaefell Summit
Length: 5 miles
Gauge: 3ft 6in
Open: Daily May to September
Facilities: Car park, shop, refreshments, museum

Opened in 1895 this electrically-powered mountain railway climbs to the 2,036ft-high summit of Snaefell, the highest point in the Isle of Man, from which there are magnificent views of the Irish Sea, Wales, England, Scotland and Ireland. The tram vehicles collect their current through overhead wires, and climb gradients as steep as 1-in-12. Five of the six operating trams date back to the original opening of the railway and are similar in style to those used on the neighbouring Manx Electric Railway (see p.126). The gauge, at 3ft 6in, is 6in wider than that of the MER, and dual gauge track is provided at Laxey where the two lines interchange. An intermediate station at Bungalow Crossing is well known as a vantage point for viewing the famous Isle of Man TT Races.

Right Car No. 1, built in 1895, at Bungalow Crossing on the Snaefell Mountain Railway *(Julian Holland)*

three battery-powered diesel outline engines. A new carriage and locomotive shed is due for completion in 1996. Visiting steam locomotives with a current boiler certificate are welcome to operate by prior arrangement.

Shibden Park Railway

Shibden Park
Halifax
West Yorkshire

Tel: 01422 367268
Route: Within Shibden Park
Length: ½ mile
Gauge: 10¼in
Open: Every weekend all year and school holidays

This miniature railway was built in the early 1980s and acquired by the present owner in 1991. It is situated in a park that contains Shibden Hall, a museum house of the 18th century. The line operates in the lower part of the park, passing the picnic area and boating lake, and gives a scenic ride which includes a tunnel, two bridges and a cutting. One 0-6-0 narrow gauge steam locomotive and a Bo-Bo diesel electric provide the motive power.

Shipley Glen Cable Tramway

Prod Lane
Baildon
Shipley
West Yorkshire BD17 5BN

Tel: 01274 589010
Route: Within Walker Wood, Shipley Glen
Length: ¼ mile
Gauge: 1ft 8in
Open: Afternoons early May to end September. Weekends October, December, March and April. Sundays in November, January and February
Facilities: Shop, museum, facilities for disabled

Southport Railway Centre

Derby Road
Southport PR9 0TY

Tel: 01704 530693
Open: Weekends June to August, weekend
afternoons September to May, weekdays except
Mondays and Fridays in June, weekdays except
Fridays in July and August
Facilities: Car park, shop, refreshments, museum,
steam rides, facilities for disabled

The railway centre is situated in the former
Lancashire & Yorkshire Railway's engine shed at
Southport Derby Road, built in 1891. A large
collection of over 25 steam and diesel
locomotives, including Mersey Railway 0-6-4
tank No. 5 *Cecil Raikes*, built in 1886, are on
display. The centre also includes a display of
railway artefacts, the former Mersey Docks
signalbox from Liverpool Riverside, a former
Midland Railway water column from St Pancras
and a locomotive turntable from York. Steam
train rides over 600yd of track within the site are
operated in the summer months.

South Tynedale Railway

The Railway Station
Alston
Cumbria CA9 3JB

Tel: 01434 381696
Route: Alston to Kirkhaugh
Length: 2¼ miles
Gauge: 2ft
Open: April to October and December. Telephone
for details
Facilities: Car park, shop, refreshments, picnic
site, facilities for disabled

The former North Eastern Railway branch line
along the South Tyne valley was opened from

Left Henschel 0-4-0T No. 14 *Helen Kathryn* and
Hunslet 0-4-0DM No. 9 at Gilderdale on the 2ft
gauge South Tynedale Railway *(H M Bell)*

Haltwhistle, on the Carlisle to Newcastle route, to
Alston in 1852 and closed by BR in 1976.
Initially, preservation of this scenic branch in its
standard gauge form was planned but this scheme
failed. A new proposal for a 2ft gauge line was
put forward and in 1983 a short length of narrow
gauge track was opened from Alston. Gilderdale
Halt was opened in 1987 and Kirkhaugh in 1996.
Future plans include extending the line still
further to Slaggyford, giving a total distance of
five miles. It is possible that one day in the future
the railway may extend even further northwards
towards Lambley, but in the meantime a footpath
follows the route and crosses Knar Burn on a high
viaduct. Many of the steam and diesel
locomotives used on the railway have been
obtained from a wide variety of sources, both in
the UK and abroad. Much of the equipment is
second-hand, and many items have been rebuilt
before being used on the railway. Included are
0-6-0 well tank No. 3 *Sao Domingos*, built in
Germany in 1928, 0-4-0 tank No. 6 *Thomas
Edmondson*, built in Germany in 1918, 0-6-0
tender engine No. 10 *Naklo*, built in Poland in
1957 and 0-4-2 tank No. 12 *Chaka's Kraal No.6*,
built by Hunslet in 1940 for a South African
railway, as well as many industrial diesel
locomotives. Many of the coaches were newly
constructed at Alston in 1991 to a continental
design. Comprehensive signalling equipment and
a former North Eastern Railway signalbox from
Ainderby have been re-erected at Alston and all
train movements are controlled from here. As
there is no car access to Gilderdale or Kirkhaugh
all journeys must start at Alston, which stands
875ft above sea level and makes this England's
highest narrow gauge railway. A journey along
the line gives passengers views of the beautiful
South Tyne valley, crossing the river on a three-
arch viaduct north of Alston, and a viaduct
between Gilderdale and the present terminus at
Kirkhaugh – once the site of a Roman fort which
guarded the ancient Maiden Way to Hadrian's
Wall.

South Yorkshire Railway

Barrow Road
Meadowhall
Sheffield S9 1HN

Tel: 0114 2424405
Open: To members only at weekends and bank
holidays and to the public on Open Days
Facilities: Car park

A large collection of ex-BR diesels and industrial
steam and diesel locomotives is housed at this site
situated on the former Great Central Railway line
from Sheffield to Barnsley. A ½-mile length of
track is home to four ex-industrial steam
locomotives, 41 ex-BR diesels (including
examples from Classes 01, 02, 03, 04, 06, 07, 08,
10, 11, 14, 20, 26 and 40) and 14 industrial
diesels.

Steamtown Miniature Railway

Warton Road
Carnforth
Lancashire LA5 9HX

Tel: 01524 732100
Route: North Gate to Crag Bank
Length: 1 mile
Gauge: 15in
Open: Weekends, bank holidays, school holidays
Easter to November. Telephone for details
Facilities: See Steamtown Railway Museum

This miniature railway operates within the
Steamtown Railway Museum, alongside the
electrified West Coast Main Line, and provides
access to other parts of the site. The line was
opened in 1980 and operates from North Gate
station, near to the main entrance, through the
standard gauge engine shed to Steamtown Central
station. It then follows a route behind the
workshops to Green Ayre which is home to the
Lancaster & Morecambe Model Engineers' steam
railway (operates most Sundays in the Summer)
before reaching its final destination at Crag Bank
where there is an interchange with the short

137

standard gauge line. Several steam and diesel locomotives work on the line, including the historic *George V*, an 'Atlantic' 4-4-2 built by Henry Greenly in 1911.

Steamtown Railway Museum

Warton Road
Carnforth
Lancashire LA5 9HX

Tel: 01524 732100
Open: Daily except Christmas. Telephone for details of operating days
Facilities: Car park, shop, refreshments, museum, miniature railway, steam rides, facilities for disabled

One of British Railway's last operating main line steam depots which was closed in 1968. It is now operated as a centre for main line steam-hauled railtours and has extensive workshop and servicing facilities, alongside the West Coast Main Line. The original running sheds, locomotive coaling tower and turntable are all still in use and steam train rides (telephone for operating dates) are given along a mile-length of track to Crag Bank. In addition to several historic main line locomotives, such as LNER Class A4 4-6-2 No. 4498 *Sir Nigel Gresley* and SR 4-6-0 No. 850 *Lord Nelson*, the centre is also home to 16 industrial steam and diesel engines. The exhibition room was established in 1989 and contains exhibits loaned by volunteers and local people. A restored and working former Midland Railway signalbox, originally situated at Selside on the Settle & Carlisle railway, is also open to the public.

Left Restoration under way in the workshops of Steamtown Railway Museum, Carnforth
(AA Photo Library)

Tanfield Railway

Marley Hill Engine Shed
Sunniside
Gateshead
Tyne & Wear

Tel: 0191 2742002
Route: Sunniside to East Tanfield
Length: 3 miles
Gauge: Standard
Open: Daily for viewing. Trains run Sundays and bank holiday weekends from January to November, Thursdays and Saturdays mid July to early September
Facilities: Car park, shop, refreshments, picnic site, woodland walks

Situated on the site of one of the oldest railways in the world, the wooden-railed Tanfield Wagonway opened in 1725, the Tanfield Railway also boasts an early 18th-century railway bridge and an engine shed dating from 1854. The colliery line was eventually closed by BR in 1968, and by 1977 a group of preservationists had re-opened the first section to the public. The line was extended to Sunniside in 1981 and East Tanfield in 1982, and a future extension to Burnopfield is planned. Beautifully restored vintage four-wheeled coaches are hauled by a very large collection of small, mainly steam, industrial locomotives. Causey station is the start of a woodland walk where the famous Causey railway arch, the world's first railway bridge, built in 1727, can be seen.

Thornes Park Railway

Thornes Park
Horbury Road
Wakefield
West Yorkshire

Route: Within Thornes Park
Length: $1/2$ mile
Gauge: $7^{1}/_{4}$in
Open: Sunday and bank holiday afternoons April to October

This miniature railway has been on its present site for nearly 40 years. The route consists of an inner and outer circle with diamond crossover providing a continuous run through the grassed park area next to the athletic stadium. The line is currently being converted to dual gauge by adding a third rail for 5in gauge trains. The larger gauge locomotives operating include a 'Tinkerbell', 'Romulus', Festiniog Railway *Linda* and *Charles*, 4-6-2 *Britannia*, 4-8-4 New York Central, and a petrol hydraulic Amtrak diesel outline.

Threlkeld Quarry & Mining Museum

Threlkeld
Nr Keswick
Cumbria

Open: Daily except Thursdays

This museum, whose theme is history of quarrying and mining in Cumbria, incorporates the former Caldbeck Mining Museum and the Threlkeld Quarry Project. A narrow gauge railway operates within the site.

Timothy Hackworth Victorian & Railway Museum

Soho Cottages
Hackworth Close
Shildon
Co Durham DL4 2QX

Tel: 01388 777999
Open: Wednesdays to Sundays Easter to end October. Other times by appointment
Facilities: Car park, shop, refreshments

A museum devoted to the pioneer steam locomotive engineer, Timothy Hackworth (1786-1850), and situated in the former home of the Hackworth family. The museum includes period Victorian rooms and some remaining buildings from Soho Works and the Stockton & Darlington Railway. Hackworth was responsible for building the first Stephenson locomotives and worked on

the Stockton & Darlington Railway as locomotive engineer. He built the first six-coupled engine, *Royal George*, in 1827 and 0-4-0 *Sanspareil*, which competed in the famous 1829 Rainhill Trials on the Liverpool & Manchester Railway. A working replica of this locomotive is housed in the museum and and can be seen operating along 400yd of track on special events days. The track runs from an 1850s goods shed via 1840s coal drops towards the present Bishop Auckland to Darlington railway line. Rolling stock is represented by a Fawcett coach, a dandy cart and chaldron wagons. Also on view are many of Hackworth's personal papers and belongings.

Vintage Carriage Trust Railway Museum

Ingrow Station Yard
Halifax Road
Ingrow
Keighley
West Yorkshire BN22 8NJ

Registered charity No.510776

Tel: 01535 646472/01535 680425
Open: Every day except Christmas and New Year
Facilities: Car park, shop, facilities for disabled

A purpose-built museum opened in 1990, which currently houses approximately half of the Trust's collection. Sound and video presentations bring the collection to life. The Trust has won several awards and its exhibits have often been used in cinema films and television programmes. The Trust owns nine railway carriages built between 1876 and 1951, many of which have appeared in cinema and television programmes, including *The Secret Agent* (1995 cinema), *Tomorrow's World* (1995 BBC TV), *Cruel Train* (1994 BBC TV), *The Feast of July* (1994 cinema), *The Secret Agent* (1992 BBC TV), *Portrait of a Marriage* (1989 BBC TV) and *Sherlock Holmes* (1988 Granada TV). Included are examples from the

Manchester, Sheffield & Lincolnshire Railway, Midland Railway, East Coast Joint Stock, Great Northern Railway and the Metropolitan Railway. Locomotives owned by the Trust include *Bellerophon*, built in 1874 by Haydock Foundry, *Sir Berkeley*, built in 1891 by Manning Wardle and *Lord Mayor*, built in 1893 by Hudswell-Clarke. Both locomotives and coaches can also be seen operating on special events days on the neighbouring Keighley & Worth Valley Railway (see p.122).

Weardale Railway Society

Stanhope Station
Station Road
Stanhope
Co Durham DL13 2YS

Tel: 01388 526262

The Weardale Railway Society was formed in 1993 to assist with the campaign to re-open the railway line from Bishop Auckland to Eastgate in the scenic Wear Valley. The President of the Society is Sir William McAlpine, with Pete Waterman as vice-President. Originally opened in stages between 1843 and 1895 to serve the local limestone quarries, the passenger service ceased in 1953 with freight lingering on until 1961 when the line was cut back to St John's Chapel. The present terminus is at Eastgate where, until 1993, bulk cement trains operated to serve the Blue Circle factory. Between 1988 and 1992 a summer-only passenger service was operated on Sundays. A fund-raising prospectus is now available from the above address.

West Lancashire Light Railway

Becconsall Station
Alty's Brickworks
Station Road
Hesketh Bank
Nr Preston
Lancashire

Tel: 01772 815881

Route: Delph to Becconsall
Length: ¼ mile
Gauge: 2ft
Open: Sundays and bank holidays from Good Friday until end October
Facilities: Car park, shop, refreshments, picnic site, facilities for disabled

Founded in 1967 by six schoolboys on a greenfield site, this narrow gauge line, situated round two sides of a flooded clay pit, obtained its first steam engine in 1969 with steam trains operating in 1980. All passenger services are normally operated by steam locomotives *Irish Mail* (ex-Dinorwic Quarry and built by Hunslet in 1903), *Jonathan* (built by Hunslet in 1898), *Montalban* (built by Orenstein & Koppel in 1913) and *Utrillas* (built by O&K in 1908). A large collection of narrow gauge internal combustion engines are on view.

Wylam Railway Museum

Falcon Centre
Falcon Terrace
Wylam
Northumberland

Tel: 01661 852174/01661 853520
Open: Tuesday and Thursday afternoons and early evenings and Saturday mornings

This attractive small museum illustrates Wylam's unique place in railway history through a series of interesting exhibits about the work and achievements of the local pioneers and local railway projects. It was opened in 1981 to celebrate the 200th anniversary of the birth of George Stephenson: born in Wylam, his birthplace, owned by the National Trust, is open to the public (Tel. 01661 853457). Other notable Wylam residents included William Hedley, who was Wylam Colliery Manager, and Timothy Hackworth who was the Colliery blacksmith.

Left Diamond crossing and restored signalbox at Marley Hill, Tanfield Railway *(AA Photo Library)*

Overleaf Orenstein & Koppel 0-4-0WT No. 34 *Montalban*, built 1913, on the 2ft gauge West Lancashire Light Railway *(J Simm)*

Scotland

1. Alford Valley Railway
2. Biggar Gasworks Museum
3. Bo'ness & Kinneil Railway
4. Caledonian Railway
5. Glasgow Museum of Transport
6. Glenfinnan Station Museum
7. Grampian Transport Museum
8. Kerr's Miniature Railway
9. Leadhills & Wanlockhead Railway
10. Mull Rail
11. Ness Islands Railway
12. Prestongrange Industrial Heritage Museum
13. Scottish Industrial Railway Centre
14. Scottish Railway Exhibition
15. Strathaven Miniature Railway
16. Strathspey Railway
17. Summerlee Heritage Trust

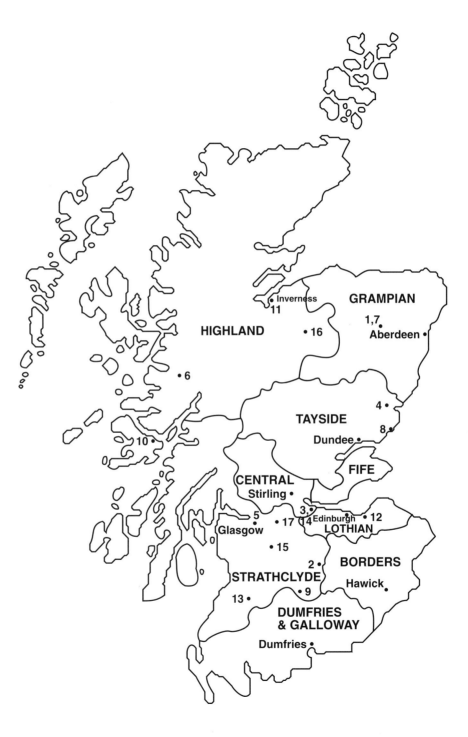

Alford Valley Railway

Alford Station
Alford
Aberdeenshire AB33 8HH

Tel: 019755 62811/019755 62326
Route: Alford Station to Murray Park
Length: 2 miles
Gauge: 2ft
Open: Weekends April, May and September, daily July and August
Facilities: Car park, shop, picnic site, museum (see p.146), facilities for disabled

The former Great North of Scotland Railway branch line from Kintore to Alford, in the scenic Don Valley, opened in 1859 and was closed by BR in 1960. Work began on building a narrow gauge railway at the Alford terminus in 1979 and now trains are operated by four narrow gauge industrial diesels and Fowler 0-4-2 tank *Saccharine*, built in 1914 for a South African sugar cane plantation. Locomotives are housed in the former bus garage at Alford. The railway is a tourist line operating in two distinct sections – Houghton Country Park to Murray Park and Alford station to Houghton Park. The Alford Valley Railway Museum is housed in the recreated station building and nearby is the Grampian Transport Museum (see p.146), with a display of GNSR items.

Biggar Gasworks Museum

Biggar
Lanarkshire

Tel: 0131 2257534 (National Museums of Scotland)
Open: End May to end September

This small town gasworks opened in 1839 and was closed in 1973. It is now an Ancient Monument and houses a museum which contains many items of industrial interest including an Andrew Barclay 2ft gauge 0-4-0 tank locomotive. The museum is managed by the National Museums of Scotland.

Bo'ness & Kinneil Railway

Bo'ness Station
Union Street
Bo'ness
West Lothian EH51 9AQ

Tel: 01506 822298
Route: Bo'ness to Birkhill
Length: 3¹/₂ miles
Gauge: Standard
Open: Weekends April to mid October, daily July and August, bank holiday Mondays in April and May. Santa Specials in December
Facilities: Car park, shop, refreshments, museum, picnic site, facilities for disabled

This former colliery line along the foreshore of the Firth of Forth was originally built in 1851 as the Slamannan Railway, being later absorbed by the North British Railway, and finally closed to all traffic by BR in 1980. The Scottish Railway Preservation Society had already set up a base on the line and re-opened it in stages, from Bo'ness to Kinneil in 1984 and to Birkhill in 1989. The SRPS collection of locomotives and rolling stock, formerly based at Falkirk were moved to Bo'ness in 1988. The trackbed from Birkhill, over the Avon viaduct to Manuel, on the main Glasgow to Edinburgh line, is owned by the railway but is not yet open for passenger services. Visitors to the railway can also visit the clay mine near Birkhill station. A large collection of finely restored steam and diesel locomotives are based at Bo'ness, including such historic items as LNER Class D49 4-4-0 No. 246 *Morayshire*, built in 1928, North British Railway 0-6-0 *Maude*, built in 1891, and Class D34 4-4-0 No. 256 *Glen Douglas*. The extensive Scottish Railway Exhibition (see p149) at Bo'ness station opened in 1995.

Caledonian Railway

The Station
2 Park Road
Brechin
Angus DD9 7AF

Tel: 01674 810318/01356 622992 (talking timetable)
Route: Brechin to Bridge of Dun
Length: 4 miles

Above Bagnall 0-6-0ST No. 6, built in 1944, at Brechin station, Caledonian Railway *(I Smith)*

Right Caledonian Railway 0-4-4T No. 419, built in 1908, awaits to depart from Bo'ness station on the Bo'ness & Kinneil Railway *(AA Photo Library)*

Gauge: Standard
Open: Sundays end May to mid September and up to Christmas
Facilities: Car park, shop, refreshments, museum, picnic site, facilities for disabled

The former Caledonian Railway line from Montrose to Brechin via Bridge of Dun opened in 1848 and was built as a branch line with its terminus at Brechin. From here another line left for Edzell and the Brechin to Forfar railway. Passenger services on the Brechin to Bridge of Dun section lasted until 1952, when many of the other lines in the county of Angus also lost their services. However the main line through Bridge of Dun continued with a passenger service until 1967, when all Aberdeen to Glasgow trains were re-routed via Dundee. A single line from Kinnaber Junction was retained for local freight and in 1979 the Brechin Railway Preservation Society took over the shed at Brechin. BR finally closed the freight-only line in 1981. The trackbed to Bridge of Dun was purchased with the assistance of Angus District Council, Tayside Region and the Scottish Tourist Board. First trains ran to Bridge of Dun in 1992 and more recently stock from the closed Lochty Railway has augmented the line's potential. Locomotive stock consists of ex-BR 2-6-0 No. 46464 (awaiting restoration), built in 1950, ex-BR diesels (including examples of Classes 20, 26 and 27) and industrial steam and diesel locomotives. Combined 'Train & Tour' tickets are available for passengers using the railway to visit the nearby National Trust for Scotland House of Dun. Future plans include a 3/4-mile extension to a new halt opposite the Montrose Basin nature reserve.

Glasgow Museum of Transport

Kelvin Hall
1 Bunhouse Road
Glasgow G3 8DP

Tel: 0141 2219600
Open: Daily except Christmas and New Year
Facilities: Car park, shop, refreshments, facilities for disabled

This excellent transport museum moved to its present site in 1989, and exhibits range from trams to road vehicles and ships. The railway section includes six historic steam locomotives, all built in Scotland, including Caledonian Railway 4-2-2 No.123, built in 1886, Highland Railway Jones Goods 4-6-0 No. 103, built in 1894, and Great North of Scotland Railway 4-4-0 No. 49 *Gordon Highlander*. Several Glasgow Underground cars and a royal carriage are also on display.

Glenfinnan Station Museum

Glenfinnan
Nr Fort William PH37 4LT

Tel: 01397 722295
Open: Easter to October. Outside these dates by appointment
Facilities: Car park, refreshments, woodland walk, nature trail, museum

The museum of the famous West Highland line is situated in the restored station buildings and signal box at Glenfinnan station, close to the well known curving concrete viaduct and the National Trust Glenfinnan monument. The museum includes exhibits showing the construction, development and present day running of the West Highland line, and in particular the Mallaig extension. Two restored ex-BR Mark I coaches serve as the 'Glenfinnan Diner', the museum's tea room, and the 'Glenfinnan Sleeper', self-catering accommodation. It is hoped to have a small Scottish industrial steam locomotive on display for the 1996 season. Standard gauge steam trains operate during the summer over the 42 miles between Fort William and Mallaig, and information about these trains can be obtained from the West Coast Railway Company on 01524 732100

Grampian Transport Museum

Alford Railway Station
Alford
Aberdeenshire AB33 8HII

Tel: 019755 62292
Open: Daily April to October

A large museum containing historic Scottish transport exhibits ranging from trams to steam rollers and motorbikes. A history of the region's railway history is displayed in the re-created Great North of Scotland Railway station which is adjacent to the Alford Valley Railway (see p.144).

Kerr's Miniature Railway

West Links Park
Arbroath
Angus

Tel: 01241 879249
Route: Adjacent to the Aberdeen to Edinburgh railway line at Arbroath
Length: 400yd
Gauge: 10 1/4 in
Open: Weekends April to September, daily July to mid-August
Facilities: Refreshments in park

A family-run miniature railway that began operations in 1935 as a 7 1/4 in gauge line, being converted to 10 1/4 in during 1938. Since opening it has carried nearly 2 million passengers. The entire route is alongside the main Edinburgh to Aberdeen main line, from the main terminus at West Links, which has three platforms, booking office, footbridge, signalbox, turntable and three-road engine shed. En route the line passes through a 40ft-long tunnel before reaching a run-round loop at Hospitalfield Halt. Six locomotives operate on the line including a steam 4-6-2, steam 0-6-0, two internal combustion Bo-Bo diesel outlines and two internal combustion steam outlines.

Leadhills & Wanlockhead Railway

The Station
Leadhills
Lanarkshire

Tel: 01461 202422

Tel: 01680 812494
Route: Craignure Pier to Torosay Castle
Length: 1¼ miles
Gauge: 10¼in
Open: Daily Easter to mid-October
Facilities: Car park, shop, refreshments, facilities for disabled

The only passenger-carrying railway to operate on a Scottish island, this miniature line was opened as recently as 1984 to carry visitors to Torosay Castle from Craignure Pier, served by Caledonian Macbrayne ferries from Oban. Building the railway involved rock blasting and crossing a bog. Three steam locomotives - 'Atlantic' 4-4-2 *Waverley* built by Curwen in 1948, 2-6-4 tank *Lady of the Isles*, built by Marsh in 1981 and 2-6-2 tank *Victoria*, built in 1993 - and two diesels, operate train services on this scenic line with its dramatic views across the Sound of Mull towards the island of Lismore, Ben Nevis, Ben Cruachan and Duart Castle. Combined sea/rail tickets can be obtained from Caledonian Macbrayne in Oban.

Ness Islands Railway

Whin Park
Bught
Inverness
Scotland

Route: Within Bught Park
Length: ¼ mile
Gauge: 7¼in
Open: Daily during Easter school holidays, weekends Easter to June, daily July to end September
Facilities: Refreshments

This miniature railway opened in 1983 and was relaid in 1989 along the bank of a river, incorporating a 140ft-span iron bridge built in 1837. Motive power consists of two diesel hydraulics and a steam 'Tinkerbell' 0-4-2 engine.

KERR'S MINIATURE RAILWAY, ARBROATH

The 10¼in gauge Kerr's Miniature Railway, Arbroath *(Kerr's Miniature Railway)*

Route: Leadhills to Wanlockhead
Length: 1¼ miles
Gauge: 2ft
Open: Easter and weekends May to October
Facilities: Car park, shop, picnic site, museum

The former Caledonian Railway branch from Elvanfoot, on the Glasgow to Carlisle main line, to Wanlockhead was built in 1900 as a light railway to serve the local lead mining industry. Gradients as steep as 1-in-35 were encountered and as a light railway the trains were restricted to a maximum speed of 20mph. At 1,405ft above sea level Wanlockhead was one of the highest standard gauge railway stations in Britain and the summit of the line, at 1,498ft was the highest in Britain. In the 1930s a Sunday service operated using a Sentinel steam railcar but trains were usually operated by a CR 0-4-4 tank engine kept at Leadhills shed. Following closure of the lead mines the railway was eventually closed to all traffic in 1938. A preservation group was formed in 1983 to re-open part of the route as a narrow gauge railway and work commenced in 1986. A limited diesel service was in operation in 1988/89 and in 1990 the railway borrowed a steam engine. An 0-4-0 Orenstein & Koppel, built in Berlin in 1913, and acquired from a Belgian museum is currently being restored. Passengers are carried in fully air-braked coaches with sprung axles. Work is currently in progress to extend the line to Wanlockhead, where a small halt will be built, and this is expected to open in 1996.

Mull Rail

Old Pier Station
Craignure
Isle of Mull
Argyll PA65 6AY

Overleaf 10¼in gauge 2-6-2T *Victoria* stands at Craignure station, Mull Rail *(AA Photo Library)*

Prestongrange Industrial Heritage Museum

Morrison's Haven
Prestonpans
East Lothian

Tel: 0131 6532904
Open: Daily April to September
Facilities: Car park, refreshments, facilities for disabled

A museum of local industry, from coal mining to weaving. Exhibits include a restored Cornish beam engine and eight steam and diesel colliery locomotives. Passenger rides along a short length of track are available on steaming days.

Royal Scottish Museum

Chambers Street
Edinburgh

Tel: 0131 225 7534
Open: Weekdays 10am-5pm, Sundays 2pm-5pm
Facilities: Shop, refreshments

Notable among several locomotives on show here is William Headley's *Wylam Dilly*, built in 1813.

Scottish Industrial Railway Centre

Minnivey Colliery
Burnton
Dalmellington
Ayrshire

Tel: 01292 313579 (evenings and weekends)/ 01292 531144 (Doon Valley Heritage office, daytime)
Route: Minnivey to Waterside (Dunaskin)
Length: 2¼ miles
Gauge: Standard
Open: Saturdays June to September, steam days on Sundays in July and August
Facilities: Car park, refreshments, shop, brake van rides, museum

The Centre is on the site of the former Minnivey Colliery, which was once part of the industrial railway system of the Dalmellington Iron Company. This commenced operations in 1845 at Dunaskin (Waterside), and as the ironworks grew so did the railway system. The period after World War I brought a slump in demand for iron and coal, and the ironworks closed in 1922. Coal continued to be mined and the colliery was nationalised in 1947. Production at Minnivey continued until 1976 and the last mine to close was at Pennyvenie in 1978. The railway line from Dunaskin to Minnivey was lifted in 1980 but it remained in situ up to Pennyvenie. In 1988 Chalmerston opencast mine was opened and the railway from Dunaskin was relaid by British Coal. The Ayrshire Railway Preservation Society took the lease of the derelict site at Minnivey in 1980 and since then it has been developed to include workshops, museum and shop. A steam-hauled passenger service operates between the Centre and the Heritage Park at Dunaskin on certain Sundays. On dates when this is not operating brakevan rides are given over a short length of the former Dalmellington Iron Company's main line. The museum, situated in the former colliery workshops, contains a collection of railway relics, and industrial steam and diesel locomotives are housed at the centre. Future developments at the site include increasing the length of brakevan rides, use of the former NCB locomotive shed at Dunaskin to display various items, and restoration of the former station building at Waterside.

Scottish Railway Exhibition

Bo'ness Station
Union Street
Bo'ness
West Lothian EH51 9AQ

Tel: 01506 822298
Open: Weekends April to mid-October, daily July and August
Facilities: Car park, shop

A new railway museum situated adjacent to the Bo'ness & Kinneil Railway station (see p.144). By using the Scottish Railway Preservation Society's large collection of rolling stock, the exhibition traces both the practical and social aspects of the development of railways in Scotland. There are also many fascinating photographs and a hands-on exhibit.

Strathaven Miniature Railway

George Allen Park
Strathaven
Lanarkshire

Route: Two circuits within park
Length: 330yd and 110yd
Gauge: 2½in, 3½in, 5in and 7¼in
Open: Weekend afternoons Easter to September

One of the oldest miniature railways, having opened in 1949, was originally of 7¼in gauge and operated steam trains along a 110yd-length of track within George Allen Park. Completely rebuilt by the present club owners, the Strathaven Model Society, the present site now includes four different gauges on two different routes. The dual 5in/7¼in ground level line is 330yd long, while the raised section of triple 2½in/3½in/5in track is 110yd long. On open days up to 20 different locomotives can be seen operating.

Strathspey Railway

Aviemore Speyside Station
Dalfaber Road
Aviemore
Inverness-shire PH22 1PY

Tel: 01479 810725
Route: Aviemore to Boat of Garten
Length: 5 miles
Gauge: Standard
Open: April to October and December. Telephone for details
Facilities: Car parks, shop, refreshments, picnic site, museum, Wine & Dine train, facilities for disabled

The former Highland Railway main line from Aviemore to Inverness via Forres was opened in

1865 and closed by BR in 1965. A preservation group started track relaying on the section to Boat of Garten in 1972 and trains started operating in 1978. The majority of the station buildings on the line date back to when the line was opened. A seven-mile extension along this highly scenic route to Grantown-on-Spey is currently being laid and a replacement station has been built at Broomhill, four miles north of Boat of Garten. The 80ft-span bridge over the River Dulnain will be the major engineering feature on this section. Train services are operated by a variety of restored steam and diesel locomotives including former Caledonian Railway 0-6-0 No. 828, built in 1899, and LMS Class 5MT 4-6-0 No. 5025, built in 1934. The railway has been used for location filming for several TV programmes, including *Cloud Howe*, *Dr Finlay's Casebook* and *Strathblair*. Historic railway rolling stock is on display at Boat of Garten where there is also a museum housing railway artefacts.

Summerlee Heritage Trust

West Canal Street
Coatbridge ML5 1QD

Tel: 01236 431261
Open: Daily except Christmas and New Year
Facilities: Car park, shop, refreshments, operating tramway, facilities for disabled

This social and industrial history museum is based on the site of the Summerlee Ironworks which operated from the 1820s to the 1920s. In addition to the extensive display of working machinery and local engineering there is an underground coal mine, recreated miners' cottages and a preserved section of the Monklands Canal, engineered by James Watt. An operating electric tramway gives visitor rides in restored tramcars from Scotland, Belgium and Austria.

Left Immaculate Caledonian Railway 0-6-0 No. 828, built in 1899, at Aviemore, Strathspey Railway *(Jim Henderson AMPA)*

Northern Ireland and the Republic of Ireland

1. Cavan & Leitrim Railway
2. Clonmacnoise & West Offaly Railway
3. Cumann Traenach Na Gaeltachta Lr
4. Downpatrick & Ardglass Railway
5. Foyle Valley Railway Museum
6. Irish Steam Preservation Society Museum
7. Peatlands Park Railway
8. Railway Preservation Society of Ireland
9. South Donegal Railway
10. The Steam Museum
11. Tralee & Dingle Steam Railway
12. Ulster Folk & Transport Museum
13. Westrail

Cavan & Leitrim Railway

Dromod
Co Leitrim
Eire

Tel: (00353) 78 38599
Route: Dromod to Clooncolry
Length: ¹/₂ mile
Gauge: 3ft
Open: Daily throughout the year. Steam trains run every weekend and on certain week days from May 1 to October 31. Diesel hauled trains operate every day throughout the year
Facilities: Shop, restored ticket office and waiting room, museum, engine shed and workshop visits, train rides

The 3ft gauge Cavan & Leitrim Railway was opened in 1887 and connected Dromod (on the Midland Great Western Railway's Dublin to Sligo line) to Belturbet (on the Great Northern Railway of Ireland branch from Ballyhaise) via Ballinamore, a distance of 33³/₄miles. A branch ran from Ballinamore, the railway's headquarters, to Drumshanbo, later extended to serve coalfields at Arigna, a distance of 14³/₄ miles, and was built along the side of a roadway for much of its length. Running through sparsely populated countryside the railway struggled to survive and in 1925 was taken into the ownership of Great Southern Railways. In 1945, when the Irish railways were nationalised, the Cavan & Leitrim became part of the national transport undertaking Coras Iompair Eireann (CIE). In later years narrow gauge steam locomotives from the former Cork, Blackrock & Passage Railway and the Tralee & Dingle Railway were used on the line. Most trains were mixed, carrying both passengers and freight, although separate coal trains were run from Arigna to Dromod where the coal was transhipped to broad gauge wagons for transport to Dublin. The end for the little line came in 1958 when a coal-fired power station, capable of burning

Left The restored engine shed and 0-4-2T No. 1 *Dromad* at Dromod on the 3ft gauge Cavan & Leitrim Railway *(G Siviour)*

3ft gauge Bord Na Mona diesel hauls a train on the Clonmacnoise & West Offaly Railway, August 1995 *(Clonmacnoise & West Offaly Railway)*

the total output of the mines, was opened at Arigna. The last trains ran on March 31 1959, the track being lifted and nature took over. In August 1992 the Irish Narrow Gauge Trust, wishing to relocate its railway museum then at Cahir, visited Dromod and found the former narrow gauge site suitable for its requirements and stock was moved to the new site by January 1993. The new Cavan & Leitrim Railway Company was incorporated in June 1993. Since then much work has been carried out restoring buildings and relaying the first ¹/₂-mile of track to Clooncolry. The first revenue earning train ran on May 27 1995 when passengers were carried in an ex-West Clare trailer. The long term aim is to re-open the line to Mohill, a distance of 5³/₄ miles, where the former station will be restored. The locomotives, carriages and wagons (supplied by the Irish Narrow Gauge Trust) are based at Dromod. Currently trains are hauled by Kerr Stuart 'Brazil' Class 0-4-2T No. 1 *Dromod* or Fowler 0-4-0 diesel *Dinmor* built in 1946. Rolling stock include historic examples from the Tralee & Dingle Railway, Isle of Man Railway and West Clare Railway.

Clonmacnoise & West Offaly Railway

Bord Na Mona
Shannonbridge
Co Offaly
Eire

Tel: (00353) 905 74172/(00353) 905 74114
Route: Circular across Blackwater Bog
Length: 5¹/₂ miles
Gauge: 3ft
Open: Easter to end October
Facilities: Car park, visitor centre, refreshments, picnic site, on-board commentary, museum, facilities for disabled

This narrow gauge railway is part of the 100-mile network of lines operated by Bord Na Mona (Irish Turf Board) in Blackwater. The lines were first built in the early 1960s to convey turf to a power station. Diesel hauled tourist trains started operating in 1990 and the current 5¹/₂-mile circular route carries passengers through the Blackwater Bog, an area rich in natural history. The route starts at a station in the Blackwater Works area and additional small platforms have been built for birdwatching enthusiasts. Special trains conveying passengers over a longer route are available for groups, and need to be booked in advance.

Cumann Traenach Na Gaeltachta Lr

Lough Finn
Co Donegal
Eire

Route: Along shore of Lough Finn
Length: 2 miles
Gauge: 3ft

Opened to tourists in 1995 this narrow gauge line has been built alongside Lough Finn on part of the trackbed of the Stranorlar to Glenties branch line of the County Donegal Railways Joint Committee which was opened by the Finn Valley Railway in 1895, closed in 1947 and was lifted in 1952. Motive power is provided by a former Bord Na Mona (Irish Turf Board) diesel locomotive.

Downpatrick & Ardglass Railway

Market Street
Downpatrick
Co Down
N Ireland BT30 6LZ

Tel: 01396 615779
Route: Downpatrick to Quoile Marshes
Length: 1³/4 miles
Gauge: 5ft 3in
Open: Telephone for details
Facilities: Car park, shop, refreshments, facilities for disabled
The Downpatrick & Ardglass Railway is situated on the former Belfast & County Down Railway's line from Belfast to the coastal town of Ardglass and was originally opened in 1892. It was authorised as a light railway to be the Downpatrick, Killough & Ardglass Railway,

sponsored by the Belfast & County Down, which worked the 8-mile branch. A preservation group was formed in 1982 with the aim of re-opening the line. Trains currently operate from Downpatrick station to Quoile Marshes, but track is currently being extended south towards Ballydugan Abbey and north to Inch Abbey. Three ex-CIE diesels and three industrial steam locomotives, including 0-4-0 saddle tank *Guinness*, built in 1919 by Hudswell-Clarke, form the motive power for the line. An interesting and historic collection of rolling stock includes examples from the Northern Counties Committee, Belfast & County Down Railway and Great Southern & Western Railway.

Foyle Valley Railway Museum

Foyle Road
Londonderry
N Ireland BT48 6SQ

Tel: 01504 265234
Route: Within Foyle Valley Riverside Park
Length: 2 miles
Gauge: 3ft
Open: Tuesdays to Saturdays, public holidays and Sunday afternoons April to September. Tuesdays to Saturdays and bank holidays October to March
Facilities: Car park, shop, museum, facilities for disabled

The museum, opened in 1989, is a centre for the former narrow gauge railways of North West Ireland, particularly the County Donegal Railways Joint Committee's lines (closed in 1959) and the Londonderry & Lough Swilly Railway (opened in 1883 and closed in 1953). A modern purpose-built centre, on the site of the former Great Northern Railway of Ireland terminus alongside the River Foyle, houses the collection on two floors which includes restored CDRJC 2-6-4 tank No. 6 *Columbkille*, built in 1907, and CDRJC diesel railcar No. 18, built in 1940. Rolling stock from the LLSR, Clogher Valley Railway and Ballymena & Larne Railway are also represented. Passenger rides are given in restored CDRJC diesel railcar No. 18, built in 1940, on the trackbed of the former standard

gauge line. Future plans include a 6¹/2-mile extension of the line to Carrigans, across the border.

Irish Steam Preservation Society Museum

The Green
Stradbally
Co Laois
Eire

Tel: (00353) 502 25444
Route: Within grounds of Stradbally Hall
Length: 1,000yd
Gauge: 3ft
Open: By appointment. Telephone for details
Facilities: Car park, museum

Opened in 1969 this narrow gauge line operates one steam and three diesel narrow gauge locomotives running on a circular route. The museum includes narrow gauge locomotives, traction engines and agricultural equipment.

Peatlands Park Railway

Peatlands Park
33 Derryhubbert Road
Dungannon
N Ireland BT71 6NW

Tel: 01762 851102
Route: Within Park
Length: 1 mile 48 chains
Gauge: 3ft
Open: Weekends and public holidays Easter to end September, daily July and August
Facilities: Car park, nature reserve
This narrow gauge railway is one of the main attractions of the Birches Peatlands Park. The 3ft gauge line runs for almost 2 miles through open bog and woodland. The track currently in use was laid in 1988, but a narrow gauge railway has been associated with the site since 1900. The Irish Peat

Right County Donegal railcar No. 18 runs along the bank of the River Foyle from the Foyle Valley Railway Museum, August 1995 *(G Siviour)*

Development Company purchased the land at the turn of the century and laid down a track to transport cut turf from the bog to a processing factory at Maghery. A total of eight miles of 3ft gauge track covered the extensive bog on which 100 men were employed. Initially the wagons were pulled by men or donkeys and it was not until 1907 that an electric system was introduced. A main generator at the factory, fuelled by turf, produced 500V dc and powered four locomotives by overhead wire. The locomotives always propelled the wagons from the rear and were nicknamed 'travelling hen houses' because of their timber structure. By the early 1950s the electric system was outdated and in 1954 it was replaced by diesels. A Planet diesel was the first locomotive, followed by a Schoema in 1956, and these operated the trains until the company ceased operating in the mid-1960s. The trains were stored at the factory but were rescued in 1981 and sent to Omagh for restoration. Passengers are now pulled by the Planet diesel while the Schoema is used by the staff.

Railway Preservation Society of Ireland

Whitehead Excursion station
Castleview Road
Whitehead
Carrickfergus
Co Antrim
N Ireland BT38 9NA

Tel: 01960 353567 (or for Dublin phone 003531 2880073)
Open: Most weekends. Telephone for details
Facilities: Shop and refreshments (some Sundays in Summer), main line railtours, train rides on site (June to August), facilities for disabled (please telephone)

The RPSI was formed in 1964 and it has always specialised in main line steam operations, running an intensive summer programme of trips out of both Dublin and Belfast. The main maintenance base is situated at Whitehead, 15 miles north of Belfast on the NIR route to Larne Harbour. At Whitehead not only are the traffic locomotives shedded, but the locomotive shed is also used for heavy maintenance. A large carriage shed is also on site where rolling stock is maintained and fully rebuilt. Annual operations commence with 'Easter Bunny' trips out of Belfast followed by the International Railtour in May. During June there are main line trips out of both Belfast and Dublin, and in July and August the 'Portrush Flyer' operates between Belfast and Portrush, as well as 'Sea Breeze' excursions from Dublin to Rosslare. Locomotives based at the site include GNR(I) 4-4-0's *Merlin* and *Slieve Gullion*, built 1932 and 1913 respectively, GSWR Class J15 0-6-0s Nos. 184 and 186, built in 1880 and 1879 respectively, and DSER Class K2 2-6-0 No. 461, built in 1922. The Society also operates about 20 carriages, which range from vehicles built by the Midland Railway in 1922, through coaches built by the GSWR in 1924/5, to coaches built by the GNR(I) and Coras Iompair Eireann in the early 1950s.

South Donegal Railway

Old Station House
Donegal Town
Co Donegal
Eire

Tel: (00353) 7322655
Open: Telephone for details

The 3ft gauge Donegal Railway system served one of the most scenic and sparsely-populated parts of Ireland and was finally closed in 1959. Based at the former Donegal Railway station at Donegal Town, where a railway museum opened in 1995, a preservation group originally planned to re-open part of the scenic DR at Barnesmore. However this plan had to be scrapped, and a new section from Rossnowlagh to Ballintra, opened in 1905 and closed in 1959, is being developed. Former CDRJC 2-6-4 tank No. 5 *Drumboe*, built in 1907, is currently on loan from the Foyle

LMS (NCC) 2-6-4T No. 4 under the overall roof of Kilkenny station on the RPSI two-day tour in May 1991 *(Julian Holland)*

Right T&D 2-6-2T No. 5 approaches Blennerville on the Tralee & Dingle Railway *(John Griffin)*

Valley Railway (see p.154) and rolling stock includes CDRJC railcar No. 14, trailer car No. 5 and a CDRJC coach.

The Steam Museum

Lodge Park Heritage Yard
Straffan
Nr Dublin
Co Kildare
Eire

Tel: (00353) 1 6273155
Open: Sunday afternoons and bank holiday afternoons Easter Sunday to end May and September, Tuesdays to Sundays and bank holiday afternoons June to August
Facilities: Car park, shop, refreshments

The Steam Museum building is built from the handsome gothic St Jude's Church, once used by the Great Southern & Western Railway's engineers. It is now resited here from its original position near Inchicore Railway Works, Dublin. The museum contains the Richard Guinness collection of historic prototype models of railway engines, including Richard Trevithick's famous Third Model of the first four-wheeled self-propelled vehicle. The Power Hall displays restored and working live steam stationary engines, including beam and triple expansion, made or working in Ireland during the 19th century. A new hands-on area for children is opening in 1996.

Tralee & Dingle Steam Railway

Ballyard
Tralee
Co Kerry
Eire

Tel: (00353) 66 28888/(00353) 66 21064
Route: Tralee to Blennerville
Length: 1 mile 64 chains
Gauge: 3ft
Open: Daily May to early October. Closed second Monday of each month
Facilities: Car park, shop, refreshments, multilingual on-board commentary

The former narrow gauge Tralee & Dingle Light Railway, which served a sparsely populated community in the scenic Dingle Peninsula, opened in 1891 and closed to all traffic in 1953. Funded by local authorities and the EU, this new line, the most westerly in Europe, has been built along part of the trackbed of the original railway from a station at Ballyard to the village of Blennerville on the coast. The line re-opened in 1993 and the route runs parallel to the River Lee through pasture land and an estuarine marsh. The area has been designated a Natural Heritage Area by the EU. Trains are operated by the original TD 2-6-2 tank locomotive No. 5, now restored and repatriated after years of languishing at Steamtown Railway Museum in Vermont, USA. Passengers are carried in carriages that originate from Spain. Future plans include a new station house and exhibition centre for Ballyard station in 1997.

Ulster Folk & Transport Museum

Cultra
Holywood
Co Down
N Ireland BT18 0EU

Tel: 01232 428428
Open: Daily. Telephone for details
Facilities: Car park, shop, refreshments, miniature railway, facilities for disabled
This large (177 acres) new museum, opened as recently as 1993 and is considered one of the best of its kind in Europe, winning the Irish Museum of the Year Award in 1994. An open air museum includes reconstructions of cottages, farms, churches, schools and shops taken from various areas in the north of Ireland. Occupying 45 acres the transport galleries include displays of all forms of transport and includes the *Titanic* (built in Belfast) exhibition. The extensive railway section, grouped around a turntable, includes many examples of Irish narrow gauge and standard gauge (5ft 3in) locomotives and rolling stock. Included are such historic locomotives as 3ft gauge County Donegal Railway Joint Committee 2-6-4 tank No. 2 *Blanche*, built in 1912, standard gauge Great Southern Railway 4-6-0 No. 800 *Maedb*, built in 1939, and LMS (NCC) Class U2 4-4-0 No. 74 *Dunluce Castle*, built in 1924. The historic collection of rolling stock includes examples from many of Ireland's narrow and standard gauge railways. Miniature train rides are operated along a 7¼in gauge line at the museum on Saturday afternoons from Easter to September.

Westrail

The Railway Station
Vicar Street
Tuam
Co Galway
Eire

Tel: (00353) 93 49253
Open: Telephone for details
Facilities: Car park, refreshments

Based at Tuam station on the freight-only line from Claremorris to Athenry. Westrail operate steam trains along the Tuam to Athenry section on selected days. Locomotives include former GSWR Class J30 0-6-0 tank No. 90, built in 1875. Rolling stock consists of ex-CIE coaches.

Index